Coast Alert

COAST ALERT

Daniel W. Anderson
  University of California, Davis
Douglas G. Chapman
  University of Washington
Robert W. Howarth
  Marine Biological Laboratory,
  Woods Hole

Published for the Coast Alliance by
Friends of the Earth, San Francisco

Scientists Speak Out

Eugene P. Odum
  University of Georgia
Orrin H. Pilkey
  Duke University
Howard L. Sanders
  Woods Hole Oceanographic Institute
With a Foreword by Anne W. Simon
and "The Home Landscape" by John N. Cole

C.F. ALEXANDER

EDITED BY THOMAS C. JACKSON, OCEANIC SOCIETY
AND DIANA REISCHE

Design by Hal Lockwood, Bookman Productions, San Rafael
Drawings by Casey Alexander
Typeset by Hansen & Associates
Printed by George Banta Company

Manufactured in the USA

Contents

Foreword   vii
ANNE W. SIMON

The Home Landscape   1
JOHN N. COLE

SIX ESSAYS ON THE COAST

Rising Sea, Shifting Shores   13
ORRIN H. PILKEY AND MARK EVANS

Oil and Fish:
Can They Coexist?   49
ROBERT W. HOWARTH

Oil, Science and Public Policy   73
HOWARD L. SANDERS AND CAROL JONES

Can Marine Mammals Survive Man?   95
DOUGLAS G. CHAPMAN

The Politics of Pelicans   117
DANIEL W. ANDERSON AND FRANKLIN GRESS

A New Ecology for the Coast   145
EUGENE P. ODUM

References   167

About the Coast Alliance   182

About Friends of the Earth   183

Foreword

The intense beauty of the coast and its great good nature in giving us its bounty have always seemed permanently alluring, ours to savor. For centuries this has been the case. In our time there has been an unprecedented act — the trade-off of a natural coast for a developed, industrial coast. The price, it now appears, is startling. No one knows what the ultimate cost will be, but consequences manifest in the last ten or twenty years are alarming enough to urge us to find out. This determination leads to new scientific insights, the substance of this book.

The coast body is sick. Most of its systems function weakly, or not at all. The coast no longer protects us from storms and floods in many places, cannot provide suitable habitats for many of its creatures. Consistently, sandy beaches disappear, salt marshes vanish, species decline; some have ended their time on earth. Poisons, penetrating deep in estuaries and offshore water, affect the entire food chain, man included. This condition, unexpected, has taken us by surprise. It has come about fast.

Look back 200 years to the very first survey of the coast, started by Jefferson, for which instruments had to be newly designed and hand-fashioned, or imported from England. Look back just a century when you could swim from the shores of Manhattan Island, and coast resorts had hardly been born; to the start of the 20th century when clubbing sea birds and shooting shorebirds were popular sports. Remember the 1920s when the advent of automobiles encouraged the first coast developments, when village fishing fleets supplied the nation's piscatorial needs only half a century before long-distance electronic fishing would compete for the world market. Look at the technological revolutions which produced the industrialized developed coast in a few decades; to the start of concern in the 1960s. Note the innocent hope of compiling endangered species lists, the false security of not including *Homo sapiens*.

Antidotes used in the past no longer work. There was a time when we could rescue an endangered species by stopping its slaughter, when we could protect a single stretch of shore or island or bay. Change has gone too far for such prescriptions.

To restore the coast to health requires a second trade-off, much more difficult than the first. We must reverse conquest and cede its gains back to the coast. Any use of the coast which destroys its natural functions must stop; uninhibited coast function must again be paramount. Known coast killers — miles of high-rise condominiums on a delicate beach, offshore oil wells, substandard tankers — can be traded for at least some degree of restored coast health. As conditions worsen, chances are that the body politic will insist on this radical bargain, even in the face of the money and power now driving against it. Across the land it's becoming evident that we need a healthy coast to survive, and the Administration that deprives the nation of this lifeline, fails the public trust.

Should we fill a salt marsh, dig for oil on the sea floor, build a sea wall? What about fish quotas, beach access, driving over dunes? How many tons of sewage can a harbor absorb without dangerous pollution? How to stop erosion, flooding, shifting sand? Hundreds of such questions multiply daily. The answers should be driven deep in the mind, be securely fastened in the law. Each decision should be based on fact, each action on known reaction. We can't afford to decide coast use by propaganda, special interest pressure, or guesswork any longer.

Some facts are known. Marine biologists, geologists, chemists — a dozen disciplines assemble information about watery happenings never even observed before, the circumstances too recently having come into being. Science has had to hurry to explore, in a very few years, conditions which have never existed on earth until now. The speed with which the coast is deteriorating and the resultant urgency to know enough to keep its systems intact, makes today's discoveries even more significant than those of other times.

New scientific insight can provide a solid base for coast rescue. Not long ago, it was thought that oil disappeared in water, forever dissolved. One of the Select Scholars says in later pages that much of it is eaten by plankton and excreted in their fecal pellets. This microscopic act is a significant fact for deciding on coast use. The pellets sink to the bottom, there to build an oil bank in the sediments, a bank of toxins regularly releasing its poison dividends. Another Scholar tells us that coast life must now adjust to an inexorably rising sea, an equally overwhelming new circumstance for the present society.

But exposing scientific knowledge to the world is itself an intricate undertaking. To dare a generalization, let me say that scientists who have made a discovery have counterculture habits. They are unlikely to grab a chance to testify to Congress or appear in the media. Instead, they become enormously busier than ever before, checking and rechecking figures, peering over the entire literature, eventually publishing their work, bulging with supporting references, in some buff-colored journal. Then, maybe, in careful quiet sentences, they will publicly discuss the new insight, new fact.

It is testimony to the thundering need to understand the coast before it is irretrievably damaged that the scholars whose work appears herein agreed to the concept of this volume. Admittedly they were subjected to considerable urging to set down for the public the discoveries they have made in the last decade or two. The book does not attempt an encyclopedic discussion of contemporary coast science. Rather, its Scholars are engaged in highly individual scrutiny of widely distant aspects of the coast. Some approach the same contemporary problem — oil in water, for example — from different perspectives. Some include philosophical overtones; one suggests that an entire environment must be restored to save a species; another questions whether whale watching, at its present all-time high, is good for whales.

As the coast degenerates, public concern grows exponentially. In 1972 the coast was granted the first national land use plan in U.S. history when Congress passed the Coastal Zone Management Act. In practice, it was hardly even a first cousin to a plan. The law simply handed responsibility for coast use to the states where, for the most part, it ended up in localities from whence it came in the first place, saturated with parochialism. For appeal to a national one-coast view, there was the Environmental Protection

Agency, the Council on Environmental Quality, the courts, and a kind of blind faith that the nation would care for the ailing coast. Then came more and more pollution, development, and the years labelled Energy Crisis with more and more oil moving and spilling into the sea, then the determination of the Reagan Administration to expand and speed up the search for off-shore oil.

These activities spawned enough discomfort and concern in the private sector to produce the Coast Alliance. The nation's august wilderness watchers and newer, activist environmental defense groups decided to unite to rescue the coast, the first such effort ever. These organizations closely cherish their own identities. Their very formation of the Coast Alliance was a sign of the deepening threat from the deteriorating coast, and the shocking absence of any clear idea of what to do about it.

Meeting over many months, the impressive assemblage of coast-concerned environmentalists collected enough money for action, scratched their heads over what the action should be. The organization pushed for protective amendments for coast programs in the federal law and a federal review of coast-connected legislation to delete some of its more glaring contradictions. Its chief effort was promotion of 1980 as the Year of the Coast "to raise coast consciousness." To a degree the Alliance did call attention to the coast and advertised its problems. It remains for the '80s for environmentalists, legislators and all citizens to decide what coast use should be, and to put that decision firmly into effect.

Throughout the earnest deliberations of the Coast Alliance, one beacon shone unblinkingly. Breakthrough discoveries of scientific fact could be the basis of action that would matter. These facts, some of which are heartbreakingly described herein, are not becoming known to the public at large for various less-than-highminded reasons. The Alliance stepped into the breach.

This book is a Coast Alliance project which could stretch to a dozen more volumes to engage the reader. We are proud to launch this first effort. A special editorial committee conceived the book, selected its distinguished Scholars and invited them to each contribute an essay. John Cole, author, editor, and impassioned coast person, agreed to set the stage in an introductory discourse. Rafe Pomerance, first Coast Alliance chairman, announced that Friends of the Earth, over which he presides, would publish the book.

The editorial committee was composed of Sarah Chasis, senior staff attorney at the Natural Resources Defense Council and current Coast Alliance chair; Thomas Jackson, vice-president of the Oceanic Society; Sharon Newsome, Coast Alliance staff; and myself. Our thanks to FOE's Bruce Colman, to Diana Reische, editor, and to Rachel Cowan for final editing and for arranging the graphics; to her, more than anyone, goes credit for the book's final form. Thanks, as well, go to Phyllis Noll and Ina Fine for helping to put the book together, and to the supporting organizations of the Coast Alliance, particularly the Natural Resources Defense Council and the Oceanic Society, for making this volume possible.

We believe it has the nascent power to start the coast back to health.

New York City   ANNE W. SIMON

April, 1981

The
Home Landscape

JOHN N. COLE

IN THE RESERVOIR of our memories each of us stores a home landscape. It's the place, as novelist Lawrence Durrell tells us, that each of us sees in his mind's eye when he orients his beginnings, when he recalls the environment that is most pleasantly remembered. It is the place our consciousness travels when it seeks to relive poignant days and nights that turned through time as easily as the wind.

For me, and for many of us I think, that place is the coast, the edge of the land, the beginning of the sea, the brink of the beach, the rim of the ocean. This intersect has a historic fascination for people; it's estimated that a majority of Americans live within a day's drive of the coast, and many of us, I would argue, see the coast as our home landscape, even if we can remember just one summer vacation. We carry the imprint so deeply, I believe, because we are creatures of the sea, because in our most primeval memories, we are there on the sand, emerging from the depths to begin our lives on land. In our innermost instincts, we have sought a return to our birthplace. We visit the coast, and we visit our genesis as well.

And on those visits, many of us acquire the home landscape that will be ours for the rest of our lives. Mine is the dunes, the ocean beach, the wind battered scrub oaks and brine-edged rosa rugosa of Long Island's eastern edge. I can, at the simplest turn of my mind, recreate the spiked, waving rows of beach grass hissing in September's gales as particles of flying sand strike the browning stems. I can see along the shivering curl of an ocean swell pushed to a perfect arc by an offshore northwest wind; just before the wave breaks, the curl catches a bit of the sun's brilliance and enfolds it, spilling it on the beach in the wave's white water.

The land is flat, so narrow, so pounded by the Atlantic on one side and washed by the Sound on the other that few trees have withstood the wind. Instead, as if the water all around wanted to reclaim its own, ponds and potholes, creeks and dreens embroider fields, snake through marshes, punctuate stands of scrub oak, and shimmer in the afternoon sun like silver coins scattered on the grass. In some places, the ponds are children of the sea and they reach rippling arms toward their parent, trying to span the slim barrier beach to reunite with the presence that created them.

My grandmother was young when she discovered such a place: the pond reaching from one side of a fragile strip of land, the Atlantic heaving on the other. Scrub oak, scotch pine, beach grass, wild morning glory, beach pea, bayberry, beach plum and cattails held tightly to that finger of sandy land, and only the great dune, rising from the beach in a curve echoing the waves that shaped it, kept the sea from sweeping in to join the pond.

Only a young woman full of dreams and unafraid of adventure would have thought to live in a place so far from the village, so near the sea. But she was a stubborn lady and years later, before I had tried my first step, I was taken from her grey, shingled house that perched like a gull on the dune and was carried across hot summer sand to the cool, wet, most delicate edge of the sea where white foam feathered shells and pebbles. There, cupped hands splashed salt water on my back and shoulders as I wondered at the sound of breaking swells.

The place was not always ours, but there was no time since that earliest summer of mine when I could not find it in my memories. My grandmother sold it; my father bought it back some years later and gave it to my mother on her birthday one July morning. I forget how many years had passed since the afternoon of my first day on the beach and that summer we reclaimed that sea bird of a house, but I know I had never been displaced. Even when the house had other owners, I would visit it. I would come in the late fall when the place was empty, shuttered, when small spills of sand sifted across the faded paint of the wooden back porch. I would sit against the shingles on the south side, in the lee, and feel the October sun on my face. From there, I could see to the Atlantic's farthest horizon — a hard edge of blue against blue. Long lines of scoters on migratory flights would rise and dip in sinuous single file as the bulky sea ducks flew just above the sea's surface. I watched entire afternoons as they stitched their invisible embroidery, and some evenings as I stayed there stubbornly, a flock of Canada geese would swing in across the beach, over the very roof of the house, so close I could see the ivory feathers of their breasts as they called and talked and settled for the frosty night in the pond behind me.

I would imagine I saw some of the same geese when I returned in early spring. By then, the sifting sand had piled into small drifts that covered the entire porch. But the warm sun would be there, the sea would always surprise me, and if the afternoon winds gathered from the southwest, they would bring the sound of geese calling and the evening would be filled with the confusion and excitement of hundreds of returning birds which had flown the long flight from the Chesapeake or the Santee looking for that finger of Long Island pointing to the first landfall of the first day's journey.

We were young men, older boys, my brothers and I, when we reclaimed the house for a full year instead of an off-season day stolen here and there. As more or less permanent residents, we became acquainted with each of the others who shared the land, the pond, the beach and the sea. We learned to name the shore-birds whose whistling calls sounded such pure, haunting notes in the heavy August air: plover, curlew, turnstone, dowitcher, sand-piper, dunlin, and yellowleg. We knew where muskrats made their dens in the cattails; we trapped eels, caught blueclaw crabs, and steered clear of the huge snapping turtles whose mossy black backs sometimes cast dark shadows alongside the flat-bottomed skiff we rowed from one end of the pond to the other.

From the dunetop we watched sulphur-bottomed whales roll and spout steamy clouds just beyond the breakers. We were there when a mako shark longer than any of us cruised in the curl of the waves, suspended in a translucent sea, gliding slowly enough so we could keep up if we ran where the sand was wet. Huffing and panting, we followed the awesome presence for more than a mile until we fell, breathless, in the wash, and the white water cooled us.

We knew the gulls — the blackbacks, the ringbills, the herring gulls and the laughing gulls. We would lie on the roof of the house in June and count 18 ospreys circling the pond until they hovered, hovered, folded their wings and dived splashing, then struggled to be airborne with an alewife flashing in their talons. We had seen sheldrake courting in March, watched hurricanes in September, and been surprised by December waves that rolled wriggling cargoes of whiting onto the frozen sand.

I was too enchanted by those times of my youth to break the spell that coast had cast. I could not, for the life of me, give it up for the city work I had been expected and trained to do. One

September afternoon when the magic of the autumnal equinox was its most bewitching, I left office, apartment, career, and peers and went back to that beach and that sea to become a commercial fisherman, to lead a life that would allow me to spend every day of every month on the beach and on the water, moving from one to the other in an endless search for the essence of the coast that had come to mean everything to me.

As a working fisherman, I began to see the sights of my youth in new perspective. Understanding the creatures of the oceans and the bays became my livelihood as well as my life. The continued environmental integrity of that slim finger of sand and the waters that surrounded it was not only critical to my way of life, but to my reasons for living as well. To fulfill my yearnings, my curiosities, my needs — for whatever reasons — to somehow become enfolded by my surroundings, the coast that had been my home landscape since my first summer had to stay as it had been since the year I was born.

It did not. It could not. I worked on that coast, and on the waters that embraced it for seven years, every day of the year. During that time, I tried not to see the changes; and, if I saw them, I refused to acknowledge them. I feared that if I contemplated any change, my experience would somehow be diluted, my focus blurred. I wanted none of that, not while I was so totally immersed in my pursuit of coastal verities. But, finally, when I had had enough, when at last I had slaked my thirst for a kind of comprehension, then I could widen my narrow vision, then I could perceive what I had been seeing ever since that summer afternoon I was carried across the hot sand, so water from the Atlantic's delicate edge could be splashed on my small shoulders.

I could see the bulldozer at work less than a mile west of the dune where my grandmother had built the first house. She had taken the risk and no consequences had been exacted. Others saw the drama of living on the ocean's brink, and they went farther along the point. One went as far as he could, stopped only by that arm of the pond that kept reaching for the sea. There, on the last high dune, he built a large house, a grand house, a place that did not perch like a sea bird, but sat heavily on the sand like a great turtle come ashore.

As if responding to that outstretched arm, the ocean often tried to cross the barrier beach at the place the pond was nearest. During most equinoctial storms, the meeting was made. Towering September swells, hurled by a distant hurricane, would surge onto the horizon, speed silently to shore and then roll across the beach almost without breaking, such was the scope of their fetch. Each of the monumental waves would leave something of the sea in the pond, until, at last, the pond would be unable to hold more. Then, as the white water receded on the ocean side, a trickle from the pond would follow it. First it would be a line in the sand, nothing more. Then, as grain by grain the sand was carried in the current, the line would become a cut, as if a heavy log had been dragged. Then a small stream would widen until it became too broad for a man to jump.

After that, the rest happened quickly. Released from its confinement, the pond pushed toward the ocean in a desperate surge, as if it feared the way might soon be blocked. The tumbling waters became a river that etched new configurations in the beach, that displaced tons of sand in hours, and often brought the ocean so close to the foundations of the large house on the dune that it appeared as if the entire structure might set sail through the surf, like our fishing dories launched across the waves.

After every blow, the bulldozer would be on the beach, trying to put back what the storms had taken. It seemed an endless occupation. When I began to perceive what I had been seeing, I realized it had been going on for years. I could see also that the mass of that last high dune was shifting; the steep wall of sand, curled like the inside of those swells pushed by a northwest wind, that hill that we had rolled down as children, was no longer so dramatic. Its pitch was modified, its curves gentled. Whatever sand was being pushed up the beach by the bulldozer appeared to be taken from the dune, even though the machine never approached it.

The high dune's slow surrender was noted at last by the man who had built next to it. He stopped the bulldozer and brought in pile drivers that upended creosoted telephone poles and pounded them into the beach in a row that spanned the breadth of his ocean frontage. Then cumbersome, tarred planks were bolted to the poles so a wooden wall was made; the space behind the wall was filled with boulders and gravel.

That bulkhead, as I recall, lasted four years, and it was not a hurricane that undid the work. A northeast storm persisted over days and nights, the wind locked in the same quarter so long that it began to move the inshore Atlantic southwest, like a river racing along its banks. These banks were beach sand, and the river-sea undercut them inch by inch, foot by foot, until the Atlantic itself began to erode the base of the first high dunes. The water wormed behind the bulkhead, pulled the sand from beneath the boulders until the rocks themselves tumbled, crushed the wooden barriers and opened new gates for the diagonal waves.

As the gales swung from the northeast to the southeast on the fifth or sixth day, and the sea moved directly ashore, there was nothing left to slow it where the bulkhead had been. And when clearing weather came, that hulking turtle of a house was so close to the brink of the dune that had once been its shield that it looked as if it could be tipped up and rolled on its back into the waves.

The bulldozer returned. The bulkhead was restored, fill was trucked in and the man who had built the house went to Washington for more fortifications. Soon the U.S. Army Corps of Engineers had built two long, lumpy breakwaters of granite blocks that poked into the Atlantic — hard, grey fingers that mocked the fluid arm the pond had extended for centuries.

Those granite groins were built after I ended my days as a full-time fisherman, but I've seen them many times. I return through the seasons and the years to walk that beach where I was born and reborn. We used to set our seine where the granite is now; it has altered the wave action and reshaped the beach. The heavy house has not tumbled and, indeed, there is more sand — but no dune — between it and the sea.

Further to the east and west, however, other dunes and other homes have fallen. One, less than two miles west, a white palace that conspicuously celebrated its luxury, was taken less than a year after it was finished. One day it was there, the next it was quite gone — the entire mass swallowed by the sea the way a mako swallows a sardine. And to the east, more homes tumbled. Some, their foundations exposed, were able to be pulled back, rebuilt further inland. Others were left for the Atlantic to disassemble, taking mantels, sills, floors, windows and walls to wherever the sea stores such evidence.

Those who lost their places, or who had seen the sea writing its message on the walls they had hoped would hold, began two kinds of protest. Some railed against the granite breakwaters there by the pond. They reasoned those barriers had somehow angered the Atlantic, broken its treaties with the beach, shifted some submerged emphasis so what had been given to protect that turtle of a house was now being taken from other innocents the length of the coast. They demanded that the groins be removed, and those demands continue. The granite fingers still point at the sea which has taken those homes.

On the other side are the proponents of groins of their own. Why not an army of breakwaters, they ask, marching in granite single file the entire length of the coast? Is it not the government's obligation, they argue, to so protect its taxpayers who build on the sand? And, as the debate echoes through the years, resounding after every storm, the sea keeps swirling at the sand.

Somehow, for reasons I do not comprehend, but which I'm certain are quite wonderful and mysterious, that place my grandmother built, the sea bird of a house, is still on its dune. Left quite untended, quite to its own passive devices, it rests now on a span that is wider than I remember. The sea, for now, has spared it. My grandmother would say she had chosen well, and perhaps she did. I look up and down the beach at the other places that have tumbled, or built bulkheads, or breakwaters, or been moved back, and I wonder why this one should survive so easily. It is magic, or dumb luck, or both — but it is there and perhaps will stay my lifetime while change surges all around. And perhaps it will not.

I believe it will stay, because I believe in the magic of the place. I must. There are so many stories I could tell. My brother, who shared those dunes, that beach, the ocean and the pond with me nearly every day of our boyhood, joined the Navy shortly after Pearl Harbor in that long ago. He served for a while as part of special Navy teams that rode the merchant ships of the early convoys — tankers that carried fuel for the war machine across the North Atlantic, troop ships, and freighters heavy with ammunition.

Early in '43, his ship was the *Blue Lick*, a Liberty Ship, one of many in a convoy that left Newfoundland on a blustery March morning. Before sunset, the *Blue Lick* was sunk by a German

U-Boat. My brother got to a lifeboat and survived; he made many more crossings and later fought in the Pacific.

In the summer of 1950, I was crabbing at the edge of the pond, near the curve of the arm that reached for the sea. As I walked the base of the dune, I saw a life preserver all but covered with sand. I tugged at it, freed it, brushed it off and read on the rotting canvas: *SS Blue Lick*. Somehow, moved by the currents, pushed by the wind, somehow that preserver from my brother's ship sunk seven years before had been brought by the sea to the one place on the entire coast where he and I could find it. It was such a shattering coincidence that neither of us ever attempted logical explanations. We said that we lived in a place we could not fully comprehend or explain.

I never forgot the incident and as the years passed, it came to have new meanings. For one, it taught me that nothing dropped into the sea is truly lost, or can ever just vanish. If a single life preserver can make an unassisted journey from the North Atlantic off Newfoundland, across a barrier beach to the shores of a small Long Island pond, then it seemed to me that everything we toss in the oceans will, sooner or later, find its way back to where we live.

That thought came to me often as a commercial fisherman. It was there when we lifted our gill nets and found them clogged with gobs of crude oil; it reappeared when I spent evenings washing my hip boots in turpentine to clean off the tar that filled their insteps — tar that had accumulated during my few paces along the beach from shore to dory. It seemed there was more oil washed ashore each year, and I began to wonder how far it had drifted, what tanker had flushed its tanks, and where.

That was before Earth Day, before the *Torrey Canyon*, before the Santa Barbara Channel blowout, and before the Atlantic along those white beaches of my fishing adventures became so fouled it was impossible for fishermen to set their nets, or for swimmers to go near the water. That day, too, came after I had left.

But I read about it, I heard about it from friends and former fishing companions who still worked the sea, the bay and the pond. From some dank hole in the Atlantic's floor off Sandy Hook, a depression used by the City of New York as its primary dumping site for 20 years, the Big Apple's offal welled and rose and surfaced. As if the sea could stand no more and vomited, the nonbiodegradable throwaways of a disposable civilization were spewed from beneath the Atlantic. Mixing with crude oil flushed from tankers leaving Perth Amboy, the mess rode a gently persistent southeast summer breeze ashore until the gross pancakes of tar and plastic drifted onto the beaches of the very people who had thrown the stuff away.

Like the life preserver from the *Blue Lick*, these synthetic artifacts of affluence found their way back to haunt their original owners. And for hot summer day after steaming day, the mess the ocean had at last rejected kept those original owners from their daily swims, ruined their beaches and made some of them think, for the first time in their glittering lives, about the wages of waste, the persistence of petroleum.

In one way, I'm glad I was not there to see it; my fishing memories remain reasonably clean. In another way, I'm glad it happened. Nothing else the ocean might have done could so convincingly demonstrate its limits to intolerance. The coast's essential fragility was demonstrated for some of the people who most needed to be convinced.

There is, however, a great deal more convincing that needs to be done. I am still incredulous at how long it has taken most people to become aware of the plight of the striped bass. That fish, that bronze and silver creature of the coast, that migrant of the ocean's edge that journeys each year from the Chesapeake to Maine, that single fish was the chief sustenance of my fishing years. It was the striper that kept me under the curl of the waves, the striper that took me back to the shores of my boyhood to set the nets of my man's work. It was the striped bass who fed me and sustained my search for myself for each of those seven years. Like the great dunes that once rose between the pond and the sea, like the pure and pristine beaches that were the thoroughfares of my soul, the striped bass was an essential of my coast experience.

Now, the North Atlantic striped bass is on the brink of becoming the first vanishing species of the ocean. We are about to exterminate a genus that has made its seasonal migrations each spring and fall for 15,000 years. No one will deny any longer that the striper population is crashing. Yet no one will agree on the cause, or even where to look. This uniquely coastal creature, this fish of the surf and white water that seldom travels more than two miles offshore, is apparently unable to maintain a rate of reproduction that ensures survival. Just as the egg shells of birds at the top of the food chain crumbled as a result of ingested chlorinated hydrocarbons, so the protective membrane of the striped bass egg caves in shortly after spawning.

We've stopped using DDT and most other pesticides that were exterminating eagles, ospreys, hawks and owls. We have not stopped manufacturing hydrocarbons, however, nor have we stopped discharging heavy metal residues into the striper's spawning waters. There are just two primary nurseries for the North Atlantic bass: the Hudson river and the Chesapeake. Several years ago, Hudson stripers were forbidden to be sold because their flesh contained such high amounts of polychlorinated biphenyls (PCBs), and the ban still holds. Spawning in the Chesapeake during these first springs of the Eighties has been the poorest since scientific records began to be kept more than 30 years ago; survival rates of the few young that are born are even worse.

The fish that sustained me can no longer sustain itself. The pure sea water that was splashed on my infant back is now defiled daily. The dunes that sheltered the house that sheltered me are being bulldozed, blown and washed away. Each of the coastal certainties of my beginnings have become the uncertainties of my maturity. The coast that made it possible for me to discover truths about myself no longer exists. It has become impossible for others like me to seek the same truths there. And this has happened within the memory of a man in his middle years. Inevitably, I must wonder what will become of this same coast if I live to be old. When I review what has happened since my childhood, I'm not sure I want to know.

Comprehending the coast's essential truths is our only defense. Just as I learned hard truths about myself at the ocean's edge, each of us must now learn new truths about the beach, the shore, the sea and their creatures. We cannot take the dunes for granted, we cannot assume the oceans will be self-cleansing, we cannot excuse ourselves by saying the striped bass, or any sea creature, will somehow take care of itself. We cannot abdicate to Nature the responsibilities we are obligated to assume.

Instead, we must grow up. We must realize there is no longer time for coastal romances and enchantments. It is coastal reality we must explore, and scientific coastal truths we must establish.

If we do not, and one day we turn to the coast in our search for ourselves, the geography of our genesis may not be there. Shortly thereafter, we won't either.

Rising Sea,
Shifting Shores

ORRIN H. PILKEY
and
MARK EVANS

ORRIN H. PILKEY

is Professor of Geology at Duke University. He spent a year as
Senior Scientist with the U.S. Geological Survey in Woods Hole,
Massachusetts and as visiting Professor of Geology at the Univer-
sity of Puerto Rico. He is also editor of the journal *Sedimentary
Petrology*, and President of the North Carolina Academy of Science.
His major areas of research are shore line geology and deep
sea sedimentology. Dr. Pilkey has written numerous articles in
scientific journals, and co-authored eight books, the latest of which
he wrote with W. Kaufman and titled *The Beaches are Moving:
The Drowning of the American Shoreline*.

MARK EVANS

is a graduate student in the Marine Science Department of the
University of South Florida. He is studying barrier island development and processes in Pinellas County. At Duke University he
worked with Dr. Pilkey on developing shoreline hazard maps for
Atlantic and Gulf Coast barrier islands.

Where the sea beats against the sand on the Gulf and Atlantic Coasts, there untold thousands of people have achieved their dream of a house or apartment at the ocean's edge. Over time, the sea has crept closer to the houses and the roads that connect them; storm-churned waves have roared through structures built upon the sands. To protect their buildings, people on many of these unstable beaches have tried various expedients: seawalls, bulkheads, revetments, groins.

Dr. Orrin Pilkey, Professor of Geology at Duke University, a specialist in shoreline geology, and Mark Evans, of the Marine Science Department of the University of South Florida, argue in this essay that such human efforts to hold sandy beaches in place are futile and, in fact, undermine the beach itself.

The authors document the theory of a world-wide rise in sea level, a phenomenon which must be acknowledged if we are to understand what is happening to our beaches. They explain how, as the sea rises, barrier islands just off much of the Gulf and Atlantic coasts migrate landward in a marvelously intricate mechanism. What seems to the uninformed to be a straightforward case of sea-beach erosion is part of a natural and inevitable shift of the entire island landward as a result of rising sea levels. Misguided efforts to stop the erosion — and therefore the island's migration — may jeopardize the island itself.

THE CONFLICT between human activities and natural forces is obvious and widespread along the open ocean shoreline. There, man-made developments imposed upon a fragile marine ecosystem create an accelerating coastal erosion crisis. It is a crisis which annually consumes millions of tax dollars; disrupts a delicately balanced environment; and imperils the lives and property of coastal dwellers. What is required is a new approach, based on recognition of natural forces, to the inevitable shifts of our coast.

Ironically, this crisis comes at the end of a decade of unprecedented growth in our understanding of the natural processes which shape our shores. Thirty years ago, many geologists and engineers believed that construction of erosion control structures would stop the shifting sands. Few regarded coastal erosion as part of a larger geologic system, as a single piece in a complicated puzzle which can stretch from sandy dunes to the continental shelf.

Today we are beginning to recognize a bigger picture, a perspective which acknowledges an interrelation of natural forces so powerful they mock meager human efforts at shoreline stabilization. Cast in this context, beach movement in response to changing environmental factors seems inevitable. If it is, we must find new patterns for living along the coast.

For generations, man has tried to protect shoreline structures with expensive stabilization projects such as seawalls, groins, and bulkheads. Often, these efforts have been subsidized with public funds. These coastal erosion control programs have not worked. Nor have they controlled the natural forces working to move the shoreline. Instead, buildings are safe only until the next big storm strikes or structures decay from inadequate maintenance. Then, the call goes out for a more complex, more expensive structures to protect coastal lives and property.

Each successive step of artificial stabilization shifts the beach farther and farther out of balance with the surrounding environment. The more extensive the erosion control mechanism, the more unbalanced the beach becomes with the marine ecosystem, the greater the potential for catastrophic resolution of the imbalance. This method of controlling shoreline erosion endangers lives, wastes public funds and does not work in the long run. Instead, existing coastal management approaches have essentially destroyed hundreds of miles of beaches in an attempt to save shorefront buildings through construction of elaborate engineering structures.

The methods tried so far fail in the long run because human effort, no matter how costly, cannot indefinitely offset the impact on the open ocean coast and sandy beaches of rising sea-level. This sea-level rise, which began to accelerate about 50 years ago, is all too frequently ignored when coastal options are discussed. Coastlines react to rising water levels by retreating landward. This shift is inevitable as long as the ocean rises. Human construction can slow the effects of erosion and shoreline retreat in places, but human engineering cannot hold back the ocean forever. To attempt to do so is to ruin more beaches with futile seawalls, bulkheads, and other human constructions.

A more sensible approach to coastal erosion requires a different process. It must start with the recognition that erosion and shifts in beaches are part of a larger natural system. Planning must therefore be based on long-term projections, not on meeting short-term objectives. The guiding principle is that human interference with the coastal system should be minimized so that coasts can achieve a natural equilibrium.

The Coastal Plain Coasts

Coastal erosion is most visible, and most easily studied and demonstrated, on the sandy barrier islands along the coastal plain coast of the Gulf and Atlantic. Understanding the forces at work on the barrier islands will underscore the urgent need for new human approaches to all open ocean beaches. Barrier islands serve as shock absorbers for the mainland against the force of the open ocean. They are both fragile and resilient. Their resilience stems in part from their ability to shift position, to alter their shapes in response to a change in their environment. Often, human efforts to strengthen island defenses against storms and erosion have boomeranged, making the island not more resilient, but ever more fragile and vulnerable to massive erosion. By pinning the beach permanently to a given line, humans have weakened and jeopardized the island itself.

Implicit in the following discussion of barrier island erosion and migration landward is the premise that, as islands migrate so must the mainland shore retreat. Studies by Stan Riggs indicate that the mainland shores of Pamlico and Albermarle Sounds are generally eroding at a much more rapid rate than the North Carolina Outer Banks are migrating. In other places — Monmouth Beach, New Jersey; Myrtle Beach, South Carolina; and the Matagorda Peninsula of Texas — the islands have caught up with, and connected to, the mainland. In other words, for short stretches of American Coastal Plain shoreline there are no barrier islands. Geologically, this is probably a temporary situation; an island quite possibly will detach itself once more as the sea-level rise continues. East and Gulf coast barrier islands are shown in Figure 1.

State	Number of Islands	Total Acreage
Alabama	5	28,200
Connecticut	14	2,362
Delaware	2	10,100
Florida	80	467,710
Georgia	15	165,600
Louisiana	18	41,120
Maine	9	2,640
Maryland	2	14,300
Massachusetts	27	37,600
Mississippi	5	9,500
New Hampshire	2	1,100
New Jersey	10	48,000
New York	15	30,310
North Carolina	23	146,400
Rhode Island	6	3,660
South Carolina	35	144,150
Texas	16	383,500
Virginia	11	68,900
18 States	295	1,605,152

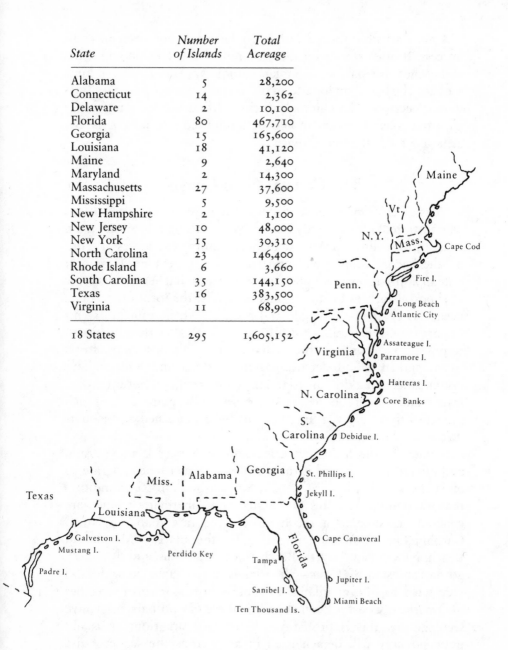

Figure 1. Representative Barrier Islands of the East and Gulf Coasts

The problems found along the shore of our eastern coastal plain can be analyzed in fairly straightforward terms to emphasize the general principles under discussion. The technical term "coastal plain coast" refers to the shorefront of the broad, flat plains found along the Atlantic and Gulf coasts. Coastal Plain Coasts are the predominant form of shorefront in this country. Other kinds of American coasts can be grouped into broad categories which range from the delta coast typfied by the Mississippi River delta to the cliff coast of California, or the glaciated coast of the Great Lakes and New England. Each kind of coast has its own unique problems, but all could benefit from the application of these general principles.

Lessons of the Outer Banks

Forty years ago, scientists and engineers agreed that North Carolina's Outer Banks barrier islands were disappearing gradually, and that drastic measures were needed to preserve these beautiful natural resources. Thus a large Works Progress Administration dune building project began. Miles of snow fences were put up to capture sand and build dunes which were then fertilized and seeded with dune grasses. For a while, the beach erosion rate was reduced, and all agreed the islands had been "saved."

Later, however, the concept that disappearing islands needed salvation began to change drastically. New research revealed that erosion on the island side facing the open ocean (the frontside) is simply part of a process of island migration. This migration is caused by, and is a response to, rising sea level. The Outer Banks are not disappearing. However, they are moving landward right out from under man-made objects such as lighthouses, motels and highways.

Equally surprising was the discovery by coastal scientists Paul Godfrey and Robert Dolan [3] that the supposedly beneficial man-made sand dunes were actually increasing the erosion rate of both sides of the barrier islands. Frontside erosion was occurring because the unnaturally long, continuous dunes acted like dikes or seawalls, and reflected wave energy. Backside erosion rates increased because the dunes blocked natural storm wave overwash of the islands. If new land is to form on the backside of the island, sand must wash over the island from the ocean side. Without new overwash sand, new erosion-inhibiting salt marsh grasses could not grow. Old salt marsh will, over a period of years, literally choke itself to death, slowly filling from too-efficient trapping of sediment until it can not stop erosion.

The North Carolina Outer Banks represent in miniature the most important practical lessons learned as a result of intensive shoreline geological research in the last two decades. The lessons boil down to: (1) barrier islands and beaches don't need human help to survive; and (2) human interference with naturally dynamic beach and barrier island systems is actually a threat to their survival.

We now recognize that coastal plain coasts are systems made up of many complex but always interrelated parts which are in dynamic equilibrium with one another. Almost anything one does to a beach or barrier island has significant environmental ramifications which affect all parts of the system. However, the time frame of environmental damage is often long (50 to 100 years), while the human time frame is short (ten to 30 years for engineers, to the next election for politicians, and until the last lot is sold for developers). As a consequence, this dynamic equilibrium receives inadequate consideration in most island development schemes.

As Glaciers Retreat, Islands are Born

The barrier islands we see today owe their existence to events occurring in the polar regions of the world. During the last couple of million years, glaciers have repeatedly advanced into the temperate areas of the world from their lairs in the far north and south. Because of the immense amount of water tied up in glaciers, sea levels drop during periods of glacial advance. As glaciers melt and retreat, enormous amounts of water are released into the sea, causing the water to rise over existing shorelines. Barrier islands form during periods of retreating ice and rising sea level. The beginning of sea-level rise at the end of a glaciation period marks the moment in geologic time that barrier islands begin to form.

Events leading to island formation occur far offshore at the edge of the continental shelf. Principal theories of how the islands form are: (1) upward growth of an offshore sand bar during a storm;

(2) drowning and eventual isolation of a line of sand dunes paralleling a beach; and (3) spit formation, i.e., elongation of an above-water sand bar which obtains its material from an eroding bluff or headland [6].

Cross Shelf Migration

Until recently it was assumed that islands formed more or less in the place they are found today when sea-level rise slowed 4,000 to 5,000 years ago. But now shoreline geologists believe that American barrier islands originally formed at the edge of the Continental Shelf thousands of years ago and that these islands have migrated to their present positions over distances sometimes exceeding 100 miles. Island migration must have been of the order of 40 to 50 miles for the Carolinas, 80 miles for Georgia islands, and more than 100 miles for some Gulf of Mexico islands. Evidence for such cross-shelf migration has been developed mostly by continental shelf geologists rather than shoreline geologists, and in this day of extreme specialization, it takes a while for the word to spread. Because not all geologists agree that islands migrated landward across the continental shelf, it is worthwhile summarizing lines of evidence supporting the concept.

Islands can migrate. Observation of modern islands indicates that migration can and does occur, hence cross-shelf migration is, at least, possible. Some barrier islands off the Mississippi Delta may have migrated more than a mile during the last century. Cape Island, South Carolina, has moved hundreds of feet in the last couple of decades.

Lagoonal shells and sediment are present on the shelf. Coring and surface sampling of the U.S. Atlantic continental shelf seaward of today's barriers reveal abundant evidence of material that once was deposited in lagoons or sounds. Oyster shells derived from lagoons provide the most solid evidence. Such widespread indicators would be present only if barrier islands were present to shield the nearshore zone from open ocean conditions.

Islands and inlets exist together. Various types of sand bodies,

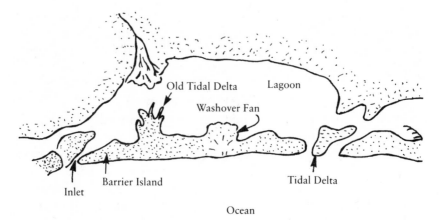

Figure 2. Processes of backside widening: barrier island migration

sand stratification, and buried channels now found on the Continental Shelf were formed in tidal inlets between islands. You can't have inlets without barrier islands. Therefore evidence of inlets is evidence of islands.

How Islands Migrate

As common sense would dictate, island migration must consist of erosion on the front, or ocean side, and deposition on the backside. Extensive long-range erosion on the frontside of a barrier can only be carried out by a rise in sea level (or a gradual and long continued sinking of the land). That's the easy part. Widening of the backside is more complex. Several mechanisms or combinations of mechanisms are involved [9]. These are shown in Figure 2 and can be summarized as follows:

Overwash.   Storm waves wash over low-lying islands, sometimes depositing tongue-shaped bodies of sand called overwash fans. Larger fans on narrow islands spill across and even beyond entire islands to deposit sand in the lagoon behind. Cape Island, South Carolina, is an example of a low, narrow island that is migrating rapidly as a result of overwash.

Tidal Delta Incorporation.   Tidal currents flowing in and out of inlets combine with wave activity to form offshore and lagoonal

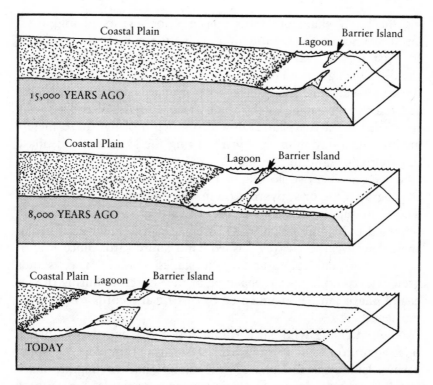

Figure 3.   Migration of barrier islands

bodies of sand referred to respectively as ebb tidal deltas and flood tidal deltas. Inlets are ephemeral features. When they eventually close up, the flood tidal delta in the lagoon becomes part of the island. Old tidal deltas are responsible for the highly irregular outline of the backside of many barrier islands.

Wind Blown Sand.   Sometimes lagoons are completely filled in with salt marshes. On Georgia's barrier islands, sand dunes blow across the islands into lagoons thus widening the islands. On Padre Island, Texas, windblown sand extends gently dipping sand flats into the lagoon, and thereby widens the island.

Fat Island; Skinny Island

A rather awe-inspiring perspective on natural forces molding and remolding America's barrier islands is gained by reconstructing the likely chain of events during 15,000 years of migration landward across the Continental Shelf (figure 3). Sea-level rise in the first 10,000 years was relatively rapid. The islands retreated rapidly. During this phase, their shapes remained low and narrow. Backside widening must have been primarily by overwash. We can refer to this stage as the *skinny island phase*. Very likely the frontsides of barrier islands down to a depth of ten to 20 meters are steeper today than they were during the skinny island phase due to loss of sand to the island.

When sea-level rise slowed, many barrier islands began a history of progradation, or seaward growth. This was the *fat island phase*. The sand supply needed for this seaward growth was probably obtained by cannibalizing the shoreface or the inner continental shelf. Fair weather waves pushed sand shoreward. Since lots of time was available because of the stalled sea-level rise, islands grew wider and higher. Steepening at the shoreface during the fat island phase can be documented by historical records from Dutch barrier islands.

Now enter the wild card. About fifty years ago the sea began once again to rise at a significantly faster rate (figure 4). As in the earlier "skinny island phase," the islands had to migrate landward. Yet their shapes — fatter with steeper frontsides — prevented the essential rapid migration. Rapid migration can be carried out only by narrow islands susceptible to overwash on a broad front. Backside widening mechanisms other than overwash are too slow to respond to a rapid sea-level rise. Hence many American barrier islands are now eroding on both front and backsides. This can be called the *slimming down phase*, an inevitable result of a faster rising sea level. As an example, Shackleford Bank, North Carolina, is retreating three to six feet per year on the frontside and ten feet or so per year on the backside.

In barrier island science, broad generalizations are bound to have many exceptions. However, one generalization that is always accurate is that no two barrier islands are alike. Some apparently fat islands such as the Georgia Sea Islands do not owe their width to the slowed sea-level rise. By sheer luck, the modern Georgia barrier islands, which are typically 100 meters or so wide, have migrated up against an ice age barrier island chain that was left

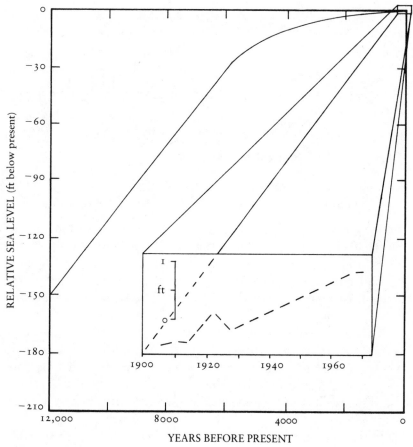

Figure 4.   Rise in sea level

stranded more than 25,000 years ago during an interglacial sea-
level high. Thus the Georgia islands are anchored by the older
island chain.

Common sense — and shoreline measurements — would indicate
that if the barrier islands are creeping landward, so must the mainland shore retreat. As we have seen, measurements by Stan Riggs
document just such a mainland retreat in several places along the
coastal plain coast. Like the movement of the barrier islands,
shoreline retreat is largely attributable to a rising sea level.

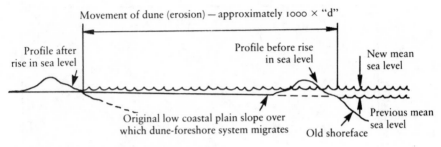

Figure 5. Sea-level rise and dune erosion

Sea-level Rise and Shoreline Erosion

Rising sea level is probably the main cause of erosion on the ocean side of American islands (figure 5). Recognition of this fact is essential, yet current strategy for shoreline erosion defense (coastal engineering) fails to recognize that any sort of sea-level rise is taking place. Since the rise in sea level is real, a successful planning strategy must take it into consideration.

Many events and factors cause shoreline erosion. When viewed in the short range, it is most difficult to sort out the effect of such events as storms, offshore topographical changes, and inlet formation and migration from the effect of sea-level rise. From a long-range standpoint, however, the sea-level rise is best viewed as the platform upon which other factors interact.

Reactions of a natural barrier island system to rising sea levels are neither constant nor predictable in the short term. Changes in offshore profiles, inlet migration, and beach position occur most dramatically during hurricanes, northeasters, and other periods of intense wind and wave energy. Between storms, the islands appear stable and development ensues at an accelerated rate. The potential for storm damage increases alarmingly.

In spite of mounting evidence in its favor, a rise in sea level remains controversial. Old notions die hard, and it is primarily the old guard of coastal engineering who hold most tenaciously to the idea that the sea is not rising, or who argue that the evidence of a rise isn't in yet. While the evidence supporting a rising sea level is not absolutely unequivocal, it is very strong.

The case has been immeasurably strengthened by recent research for the National Academy of Science and the President's Council on Environmental Quality. The "Greenhouse Effect" is the suspected villain [10]. The increased carbon dioxide content of the atmosphere produced by combustion of fossil fuels is warming up the earth and melting polar ice caps. The prognosis is for a prolonged, even accelerated, sea level rise.

Further supporting evidence comes from other indicators:

Tide gauge data.   The only way to measure short term sea-level changes is by direct measurement of daily tidal fluctuations. Stacey Hicks of the National Oceanic and Atmospheric Administration [5] observed that at a number of locations along the tectonically stable East and Gulf Coasts, tide gauges show a generally similar curve of sea-level rise. Such evidence doesn't automatically answer the sea-level rise question because tide gauge sea-level data can be misleading. Climate, wind and runoff pattern changes, upstream and downstream alterations in river channel characteristics, and harbor dredging all can cause apparent changes in sea level. However, the consistency of Hicks' data from place to place strongly argues that the sea-level rise is real. Recently, Ken Emery of Woods Hole Oceanographic Institution [4] has noted an essentially identical, accelerating sea-level rise in tide gauge records from Asian Pacific harbors.

Barrier island retreat is ubiquitous.   Our beaches are behaving as if the sea level is rising. The frontsides of almost all American barrier islands (as well as other types of shorelines) are eroding at rates ranging from one foot to fifty feet per year. Perhaps a figure between two and three feet is the national barrier beach average annual recession rate. Probably less than 10 percent of our barrier shoreline is static or growing seaward. By far the best explanation for a worldwide shoreline erosion trend is rising seas. Local exceptions can be explained either by temporary special circumstances such as sand supply and wave refraction. Local variations in apparent sea-level rise rates may be related to relatively rapid uplift or sinking of the land (tectonic uplift).

Indirect evidence.   Along the Pamlico and Albermarle Sounds of the North Carolina shoreline, pine trees are dying on the margins of salt marshes. According to geologist Stan Riggs, this pine mortality is very probably a reflection of gradual ocean rise which causes a slightly increased frequency of salt water flooding as well as a rising of the groundwater table. Peter Rosen's detailed study of erosion along the shores of Chesapeake Bay indicates that rates of erosion of the various types of shoreline can best be explained by a sea-level rise. That is, differing rates of erosion are not a simple function of resistance of the material to wave attack.

If the sea level is rising and if the beach-barrier island-continental shelf system is shifting to accommodate this factor, then we should follow suit and change our pattern of utilizing the fringe of our coastal plain coasts. A key element of this new approach to the shore must include the realization that engineering strategies cannot provide long-range solutions for restless coasts. The philosophy of thwarting natural forces with engineering devices must give way — if only for its enormous environmental and economic expense — to planning less human interference in dynamic shoreline systems.

People and Barrier Islands

In order to live harmoniously with a barrier island it is first necessary to recognize that the island is like a well-oiled machine with interdependent parts. A barrier island exists in a dynamic equilibrium between sand supply, wave energy, tides, winds, vegetation types, and other factors. A change in one factor causes the others to shift and in some way adjust. This "adjustment" may be a profound event from the standpoint of a beach cottage owner.

A particularly spectacular illustration of the consequences of misunderstanding the dynamic equilibrium of an island involves the Army Corps of Engineers and Wrightsville Beach, North Carolina [13]. In defense of the Corps, it should be noted that the project was carried out before we understood the role of tidal deltas in the barrier island equilibrium scheme.

In the mid-1960's Moore's Inlet, separating Wrightsville Beach and Shell Island, was filled in by dredging sand from the backside

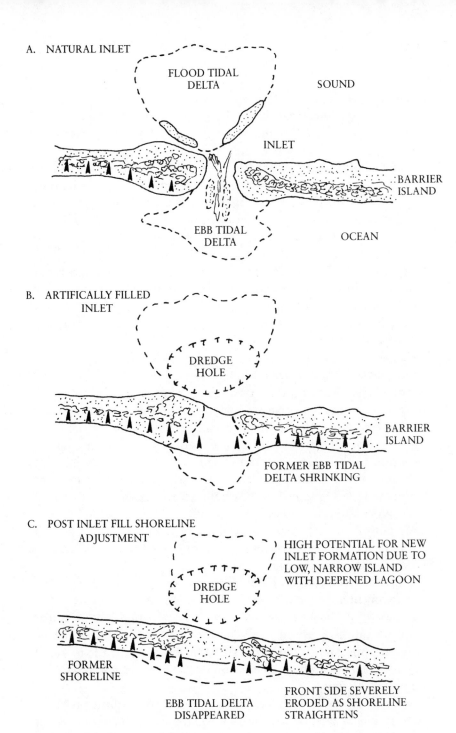

A. NATURAL INLET

FLOOD TIDAL
DELTA

SOUND

INLET

BARRIER
ISLAND

EBB TIDAL
DELTA

OCEAN

B. ARTIFICALLY FILLED
INLET

DREDGE
HOLE

BARRIER
ISLAND

FORMER EBB TIDAL
DELTA SHRINKING

C. POST INLET FILL SHORELINE
ADJUSTMENT

HIGH POTENTIAL FOR NEW
INLET FORMATION DUE TO
LOW, NARROW ISLAND
WITH DEEPENED LAGOON

DREDGE
HOLE

FORMER
SHORELINE

EBB TIDAL DELTA
DISAPPEARED

FRONT SIDE SEVERELY
ERODED AS SHORELINE
STRAIGHTENS

Figure 6. Filling Moore's Inlet

of the island (figure 6). The sand was obtained by complete removal of the flood tidal delta, the body of sand pushed into the
lagoon by currents flowing through the inlet. This was major
mistake number one. On islands along this portion of the North
Carolina coast, old tidal deltas, which soon become broad ex-
panses of salt marsh widening the island, are essentially immune
to new inlet formation during hurricanes. Removing the sand
removed this hurricane protection. Inlets form in the last stages
of a hurricane, when water, driven by winds into a lagoon or
estuary system, rushes back catastrophically, slicing through the
island on its return to the sea. Digging a deep hole behind a particular portion of an island has the effect of furnishing a potentially
large volume of water to aid in inlet formation. Thus not only was
protection removed, but the danger of major storm damage was
actually enhanced.

That's not the whole story. At the time Moore's Inlet was
closed, an ebb tidal delta, a body of sand, existed on the frontside
of the island. With no inlet tidal currents to shift sand in an offshore direction, this offshore body of sand quickly disappeared,
wave refraction patterns changed, and rapid erosion of the frontside ensued. Unfortunately, before nature straightened out the
frontside of the island, humans divided the island front into lots
and built beach cottages. The houses are now in the surf zone.
Incidentally, a Holiday Inn was built on the exact site of the old
inlet. Inevitably, the motel has been dubbed the Holiday Innlet.

Wrightsville Beach is not an isolated case. In the past, very little
of the development on American barriers has been based on any
understanding of how islands work.

Unfortunately, the same holds true today.

Human interaction with barrier islands — and with the rest of
the coast — can be either active or passive. The building of houses
or beach cabins is essentially a passive interaction, but when it's
done on a migrating, dynamic island, it inevitably leads to active
intervention. The human role becomes active as we try to stabilize
the beach or island.

So long as we do not actively try to control natural processes
such as beach erosion on barrier islands, humans probably do
little fundamental damage to the island geologic system. Aesthetics

aside, even heavy development probably does not prevent the island from migrating and evolving in some fashion, even if different from the way the island would have evolved in its natural state. Islands survive naturally under an amazing variety of conditions of wave energy, sand supply, climate, and vegetation types. When humans remain in passive roles, their changes can be absorbed by most islands. In such cases, people probably do more damage to themselves and their accoutrements than to the island system.

That's because developers almost inevitably subdivide islands into rectangular lots just as though they were selling part of a Kansas wheat field. They fail to recognize that a barrier island consists of many sub-environments, each with differing dynamic characteristics. We have not always been this foolish — or greedy.

In the early days, up to the 1950's, lots sold in Nags Head, North Carolina, were narrow and long so homeowners could move their houses back in response to an eroding shoreline. The Outlaw family home was moved three times in 100 years, a distance of 200 feet each time. Since the house is now threatened again by the surf zone, shoreline movement of six feet per year is indicated. But nowadays the lots sold on Nags Head are about the same size and shape as those in a St. Louis, Missouri, suburban housing development.

Usually the higher-risk lots sell for steeper prices because they have a better view. Examples of particularly dangerous environments for building lots include overwash passes, narrow island stretches susceptible to inlet formation, island extremities susceptible to inlet migration, and active sand dunes. Many Texas barrier islands have "passes," which are low zones through which water rushes back to sea after major storms. Although these passes flood repeatedly, houses and even condominiums have been built in them. In one case a seawall has been built in front of a condominium located in a "pass." The owner undoubtedly did not realize that the enemy was to the rear. The seawall can be expected to act as a dam to backrushing waters after the next storm, flooding the condominium. It should be noted that on most Atlantic barriers, prediction of major overwash or backwash locations is much more difficult than on Texas barriers.

A more fundamental problem is caused by emplacement of utilities such as water pipelines through areas of potential destruction. A good example is the water pipeline connecting Buxton and Avon, North Carolina. Immediately north of Cape Hatteras the pipeline goes through a narrow portion of the island which overwashes repeatedly and which has high potential for inlet formation. When, as is inevitable, either shoreline erosion or formation of an inlet takes out the pipeline, an equally inevitable change will occur. The inlet will be "repaired," shoreline erosion will be stopped, and man will have begun to "stabilize" the island.

To reemphasize, however, human development on a barrier island is not fundamentally destructive to an island as long as the development remains passive, as long as man does not interfere and actively try to halt the barrier island migration processes. This interference with island processes to maintain status quo is called "stabilization" by engineers.

In early decades, barrier island dwellers either lived in "safe" areas, such as maritime forests on the backsides of wide islands, or they watched as their houses fell in when the shoreline retreat "caught up." The likelihood of modern Americans adopting a "live with nature" philosophy, as did the old island dwellers, sometimes seems as remote as stopping the sunset. Much publicity has been given in recent years to the concept of setback lines as an approach to environmentally sound island development. What happens, however, when sea-level rise chews up the setback line in ten or 40 years? A state's coastal zone management policy would have to be tough indeed to compel the captains of American industry, the pillars of local society, and the cream of local politics to move their houses or let them fall into the sea, or to outlaw the building of seawalls. For practical purposes it is fair to say that a passive, nonintervening relationship between modern man and a barrier island does not now exist. Instead we actively disrupt natural coastal systems at great environmental and economic cost.

New Jerseyization, or the Concrete Coast

Most geologic research has been carried out on pristine and undeveloped islands. Hence the effect of development on islands

Figure 7. New Jerseyization at Monmouth Beach, New Jersey

and island processes must be shown by comparison with processes studied on islands unencumbered by humans. The emerging conclusion from such comparisons is that stabilization of barrier islands results in fundamental damage to the island at great cost to taxpayers.

One could argue that such conclusions do not require particularly great scientific insight. After all, even casual observation of our oldest developed barrier island shorelines reveals a problem. Why else are the seawalls so thick, the beach in front of them so ravaged? The term that is increasingly used to describe this problem is "New Jerseyization," the final stage of barrier island stabilization (figures 7, 8, 9).

A New Jerseyized beach is a beach fronted by a large sea wall. Rubble from pre-existing seawalls, groins, revetments, etc. clutter the beach in front of the sea wall. On most such beaches no sand

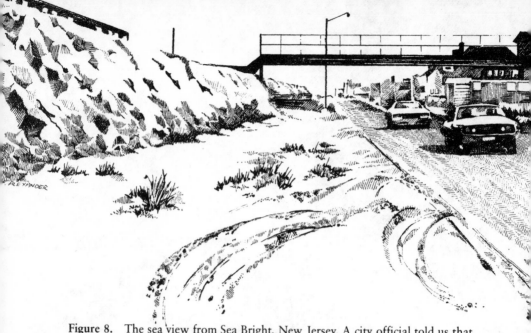

Figure 8. The sea view from Sea Bright, New Jersey. A city official told us that "once there were not only houses in front of where the sea wall is, there were farms out there." Now 25 knot winds produce sea wall topping waves. This community has been New Jerseyized.

Figure 9. A New Jersey Island after the 1902 Ash Wednesday storm. It is clear in this photograph how the unstabilized and undeveloped portion of the island has migrated while the stabilized portion has remained in place. In a long range sense (50 to 100 years) the developed portion is becoming increasingly out of equilibrium with the rising sea level. Presumably as time goes on the community will be forced to go to increasingly extensive and expensive shoreline fortification to protect "themselves." From an Army Corps of Engineers photo.

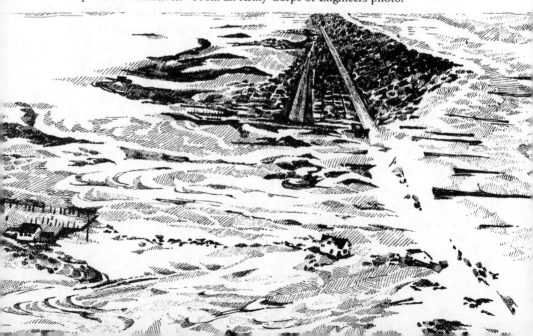

is visible except, perhaps, at extreme low tide. The shoreface has steepened considerably and, as a result, wave energy is high. No longer do large waves trip over offshore sand bars. Instead, all waves — large and small — impinge directly on the sea wall and are reflected onto a narrowed and usually submerged beach at the foot of the seawall.

Why have we done this to once-sandy beaches? Most island stabilization schemes result from human efforts to stop erosion on the open ocean shore. When this frontside erosion threatens buildings, attempts are made to stop it. Stabilization efforts can be either structural or non-structural. The non-structural approach is always preferable and consists of beach replenishment or building a new beach with sand dredged from behind or in front of the island (figure 10). Even the relatively gentle, non-structural approach of beach replenishments unbalances the island's equilibrium.

The out-of-equilibrium island, stabilized by structural means, responds by steepening of the shoreface. The steepening is caused at least in part by reflection of wave energy from sea walls and other shorefront structures. The sand lost during shoreface steepening may disappear in an offshore direction or into tidal deltas inside lagoons.

There are two basic approaches to structural stabilization of beaches: either (1) build walls (groins) perpendicular to the beach to trap sand and hence build up the beach, or (2) build walls parallel to the beach (seawalls) to block wave energy (figure 11). After this human tinkering, the beach cannot respond in normal ways during storms. Storm waves on a sea-walled beach are blocked from chewing into the dunes, their normal source of sand for flattening.

Over the years the shoreface becomes steeper, wave energy continues to increase and the old seawall is breached or damaged. In response, sea walls must be built wider, higher, stronger. The island becomes a stabilized fortress. No alternatives exist other than to continue building bigger and better sea walls. The seawall approach is the most drastic one and is usually done as a last resort (figure 12). All who have studied the shoreline agree sea walls destroy beaches.

Figure 10. A modest beginning of New Jerseyization on Topsail Island, North Carolina. The owner of the threatened structure has hired a bulldozer to "readjust the beach profile in his favor." However it is now believed that pushing sand from the lower to the upper beach may actually increase the rate of erosion during the next minor storm. From a photo by Duncan Heron.

Stabilization is irreversible. A long-stabilized island will be so far out of equilibrium with the level of the sea that removal of the sea walls would probably cause the island to disappear quickly. Why is the situation irreversible? Artificial sand replacement to restore the beach is volumetrically and economically out of the question. Small beach replenishment projects would disappear rapidly down the steep shoreface. Restoration of the old island dynamic equilibrium by natural means is politically out of the question because large numbers of buildings would have to be moved, destroyed, or allowed to fall into the sea.

The above sequence of events on the open ocean shoreline is now well established and agreed upon by most shoreline geologists and engineers. Yet seawalls continue to sprout on our open ocean shorelines at an increasing rate. Hurricane David fathered at least three new seawalls, including one in front of the most exclusive section of Sea Island, Georgia. Part of the problem, again, is the short-range view. Owners of $200,000+ homes with a sea view are understandably unwilling to allow their houses to tumble into

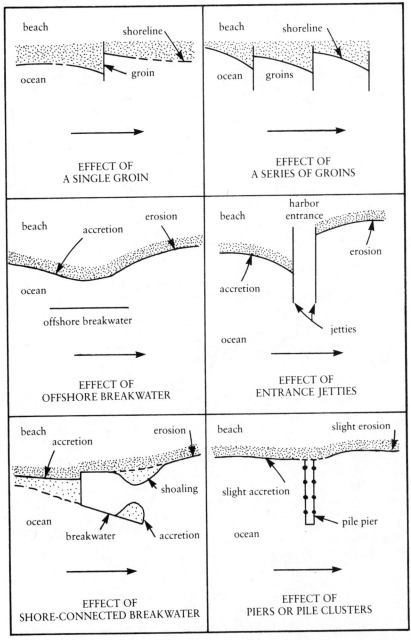

Figure 11. Examples of how shoreline engineering structures work. Groins, breakwaters and jetties and even fishing piers trap sand and build up the beach at selected localities. The beach build-up is good both from a recreational and a storm protection standpoint. A problem arises however because the trapped sand is "robbed" from someone else's beach or island. The "robbed" beach undergoes erosion because its sand supply is reduced.

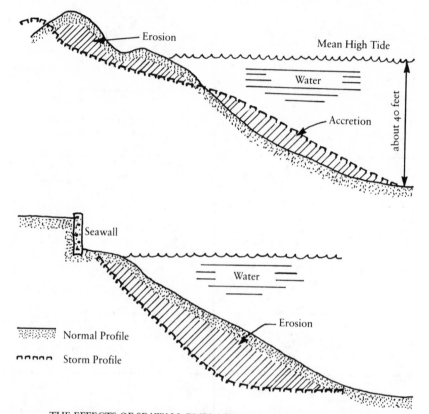

THE EFFECTS OF SEAWALL EMPLACEMENT ON BEACH PROFILES

Figure 12. Comparison of storm response of a seawalled beach and a natural beach. The natural beach flattens out during a storm by transferring sand from the upper beach and dune to the lower beach. By flattening the beach, wave energy is dissipated over a broad surface. It is a beautiful mechanism of self-preservation, almost as if the beach can think for itself. The seawalled beach cannot respond to the storm. Instead, with each important storm the beach becomes steeper and sand is permanently lost.

the sea (even with federal flood insurance to pay the cost). Thus the New Jerseyization process begins.

Economics may ultimately compel coastal science to be brought to bear on development plans. The first bureaucratic ray of hope came in 1972 with the cautious beginning of a National Park Service policy of keeping hands off barrier islands. Careful studies by Robert Dolan and Paul Godfrey indicated the long-range cost of halting erosion to be high while the likelihood of success is nil. On a cost-effectiveness basis, then, coastal stabilization scores very poorly.

At the heart of the problem is the fact that none of our present approaches to the open ocean shoreline addresses the reality of the rising level of the sea. Stabilization simply stops an island from migrating. The whole island system then becomes increasingly "out-of-equilibrium" with the sea level. Putting it another way, the island is forced to remain in an increasingly vulnerable location. We should not forget that a "barrier island" is just that — a frontline barrier to keep the forces of the open ocean from the mainland itself. As the islands are weakened and made vulnerable by human tinkering, the danger of massive storm damage increases — both to the island and to the mainland behind.

While we have concentrated on barrier beaches, it must be repeated that the similar processes work on mainland shorelines. Erosion landward has been observed at many points along the eastern and Gulf coastal plain coasts. To ignore the fact that erosion is inevitable as long as the sea rises is to invite further coastal disaster.

Geologists vs. Engineers

A major problem confronting those concerned with the coast is disagreement between scientists and engineers on how to "solve" the "erosion problem." Engineers tend to take a problem-solving position, which suggests that barrier island stabilization is a reasonable solution for a coast in crisis. For obvious reasons, this solution is the most favored by politicians faced with endangered houses and angry shoreline owners. Basically, engineers are doing what most shoreline dwellers want them to do: saving buildings from destruction. The alternative geological solution encompasses a much longer time frame. The geological solution finds few adherents among coastal dwellers because it says there is no "solution." Nothing should be done to save these structures.

The following quotes from engineers will help explain the problem of communications between engineers and geologists, and between those who adopt a short term view of coastal issues and those who adopt a more far-sighted "hands-off" approach. Inevitably, these statements are, to some extent, out of context. Our purpose is not to belittle those quoted, but rather to illustrate the nature and magnitude of the gulf between shoreline engineers and geologists.

> "The subject of sea-level hardly warrants comment. . . . [Problems caused by rising sea level] will be solved by future generations."
>
> Author of Coastal Engineering textbook

Many engineers agree that the sea-level rise is a major factor in shoreline erosion. Unfortunately many disagree. In any case, shoreline engineering research has so far ignored sea-level rise in favor of short-range solutions. The second part of the statement is perhaps the very essence of the engineering mentality. It may be the confidence that a future generation will solve problems which has helped produce our high standard of living. But along the American shoreline, the future has arrived in the form of stone and concrete beaches. We *are* the future generation, and there is nothing we can do to alter the magnitude of environmental disaster caused by trying to hold back the sea with man-made structures.

> "This project [the $65 million replenished beach at Miami Beach] should last indefinitely providing a major storm doesn't come by."
>
> Miami District Corps of Engineers official

One need not be a geologist to know that storms are part of the natural system, and therefore inevitable. Storms are part of the equilibrium in which islands and coasts exist. In places like Core Banks, North Carolina, the vegetative cover over much of the island is adjusted to, and even requires, occasional innundation by storm overwash. There is much to learn about the effect of storms in transporting sand, both within the littoral zone and to and from the continental shelf.

Engineers know storms will occur. Storms are factored into the design criteria of the various stabilization schemes. By semantic slight of hand, however, these inevitable storms are made to seem remarkable and unpredictable. When "natural disaster" strikes and destroys a sea wall or groin, the storm is called an "act of God," and thus a technical challenge to be met.

"In our national studies as well as in my own extensive coastal engineering experience in this field I have never heard of engineering or geological studies which show that such revetments damage or diminish the beach."

Member, U.S. Shoreline Erosion Advisory Panel

Revetments are usually constructed of uncemented large boulders on the face of the seaward dune or bluff. Boulders are piled in a slope downward toward the water. During storms, revetments prevent shoreline retreat and also minimize wave reflection problems because water from breaking waves is "absorbed" into the interstices between boulders. It is probably true that there are no studies indicating that revetments cause erosion, because a direct relationship would be difficult to prove. However, judging from well-known shoreline principles, revetments should cause severe erosion in the long run.

The best place to see this demonstrated is along the Massachusetts shoreline. Many houses have been built on actively eroding piles of sand and gravel left behind by retreating glaciers. Every storm cuts back into the unconsolidated bluffs and supplies fresh material for the beaches. To prevent their homes from falling into the water, homeowners have built revetments at the base of many bluffs. The house is saved. However, the beach is starved of its normal building material. To one degree or another, revetments on the front of barriers will cause sand starvation, especially during a rise in sea level.

Revetments probably also cause erosion by preventing normal storm response by the beach. The revetments prevent storm waves from collecting the required sand from dunes to flatten the beach. The beach remains too steep during storms and a permanent loss of sand to the continental shelf probably occurs.

From a geological viewpoint, the idea that revetments don't cause erosion is absurd. Yet in an abbreviated time frame (say, 20 years), they seem to be effective. The effect of revetments on the beach would be expected to be manifested much more slowly than that of a sea wall. So once again the disagreement between geologists and engineers reflect a difference in the context of time over which the issue is viewed.

"Examples of recent attempts to cooperate with nature are bypassing of littoral sand at jettied inlets, nourishment of beaches using suitable sand fill mined from adjacent continental shelf areas, construction of offshore breakwaters to act as headlands, creation and stabilization of dunes by selective grass planting and the use of special dredges to recycle clean sand from navigation channels to downdrift beaches."

Geologist, U.S. Army Corps of Engineers,
Coastal Engineering Research Center

All procedures listed in this quotation are attempts to prevent the shoreline from moving landward in response to sea-level rise. As mentioned earlier, under conditions of the present sea-level rise rate, the horizontal movement should be of the order of 100 to 1,000 feet per century, clearly an impressive figure. These approaches listed by this Corps of Engineers scientist ignore the fact that the sea-level is rising. Yet the longer a shoreline is held in position, the further it will be out of equilibrium; the more pressure there will be to build bigger, stronger defenses; the closer the shore will be to New Jerseyization. Just as the geologist's remark shows that not all geologists decry stabilization, it is also true that not all engineers support shoreline stabilization. In fact, the concept of the equilibrium beach moving landward with sea-level rise is the product of the fertile mind of Dr. Per Bruun — a coastal engineer [1].

Farewell to the Concrete Beach

If our ocean shore is not to be a wall of ugly concrete, rubble, and stone, the solution is a two-pronged one. Immediate steps must be taken to change present development practices on islands and other exposed coasts. Then, because the geologist's view is largely a qualitative one which is unconvincing to coastal dwellers and the engineers they hire, research is needed to document in a quantitative way the negative effects of anchoring a beach in place through stabilization.

The obvious solution to New Jerseyization is simple; stop all island and coastal stabilization projects. Let the ocean and shore reach an equilibrium. This, however, is a multi-edged sword. To allow natural forces to work on the coasts (the new Park Service policy on islands) collides with the classic American belief that technology — and money — can solve most problems.

> "This do-nothing philosophy may have suited the times of King Canute in the 11th century where population was limited and few people had time or inclination to visit the coast, but it is unacceptable to the general public in 20th century America where the federal government has taken the responsibility to provide for the general public welfare."
>
> Geologist, U.S. Army Corps of Engineers,
> Coastal Engineering Research Center

Once again, this statement is understandable if one views the coastal crisis in short-range context. However, the hands-off approach appears less outrageous and perhaps a bit more realistic in the context of the long-range aesthetic, environmental and economic effects of New Jerseyization. The apparently irreversible steepening of the shoreface on islands protected by seawalls and groins is a strong argument against any sort of barrier island stabilization. To do nothing, and hence to prevent such steepening, however, endangers and eventually dooms structures on the open ocean shore.

There are many ways to implement our geological approach including letting the ocean claim endangered houses (most are covered by Federal Insurance), subsidizing the moving of houses, forbidding construction near a beach (a temporary solution on a migrating island), and preventing coastal houses destroyed by storms from being replaced.

In such an approach, even private landowners should not be allowed to stabilize their shorefronts. If the owners are wealthy enough to put in substantial structures such as those at East Hampton, New York, or Sea Island, Georgia, New Jerseyization will begin even without the mighty presence of the federal government. Less wealthy homeowners will simply build flimsy structures that are quickly destroyed and scattered over the beach in the next storm. Folly Beach, South Carolina, comes to mind.

"Do nothing" means also that new inlets must be allowed to form in storms; old inlets must be allowed to migrate or to close naturally. Inlets must be studied individually and development should not be permitted in possible paths of inlet migration. Access roads and main utility lines should be perpendicular to the island, and should not run parallel with the island where they are more vulnerable. If such access is planned with likely points of new inlet formation in mind (based on studies of the particular island), minimum disruption will occur when the inlets form. It will then be feasible to allow the inlets to remain naturally open. We should never bridge inlets. If an inlet must be crossed, let it be by ferry.

The concrete coast is not simply an engineering phenomenon. It is also a product of politics. A great deal of clout is needed to get the tax support required to pay for expensive groins and sea-walls along miles of open ocean beaches. If we are to prevent this New Jerseyization, we must counter the powerful forces that argue for spending public money on unwise and expensive building projects to anchor the shoreline. An additional political approach would be to prohibit development on heretofore unbuilt-up islands. We could decide that there will be no federal expenditures on barrier islands. Either of these actions would have the same result. Without federal expenditures on bridges, sea walls, beach replenishment, highways, water and sewer systems, flood insurance, and storm recovery, the dynamic equilibrium of most islands would be undisturbed. On the other hand, light development up to the island's natural carrying capacity, in terms of water and sewage, could well occur without the aid of the federal government.

Perhaps the most difficult (if not impossible) concept for island dwellers to grasp is that nothing is permanent on a barrier island —or on most other coasts exposed to the open ocean. Fishermen, marina owners, and residents should be prepared for business failure or relocation when an inlet closes. Fisheries in lagoons must be adjusted according to the changes in inlet locations and water salinities. Historical lighthouse buildings cannot be preserved. Bridges and highways may have to be moved or replaced.

Research Needs

Perhaps the most important of all solutions to New Jerseyization is to address the issue of the sea-level rise in all barrier development schemes. Research to help establish sound coastal policies should include many vital areas.

Alternative responses to the sea-level rise.   Three possible ways of responding to higher sea levels are to do nothing at all, to foster artificial migration, or to establish minimum standards of engineering for all coastal structures. Artificial migration has been suggested by the Park Service for the Fire Island National Seashore in New York. Instead of the long range futility of pumping sand on the frontside, they propose to dump intracoastal waterway dredge spoil on the backside, thus "helping" the island to migrate.

The minimum standard concept is one which would allow persons to build "weak" structures to halt erosion. Such structures, perhaps, could be designed to withstand a storm of the intensity that occurs only once every five years, but would be cleared away by a ten-year storm.

Documentation and quantification of long range effects of various stabilization techniques.   This research will allow citizens at barrier island and other exposed ocean communities to make better long range decisions. Ocean City, Maryland, could have used such information very recently. The Corps has proposed a combination of beach replenishment and massive bulkheads as a "permanent solution" to their erosion problem. On the contrary, experience in many areas clearly shows that the bulkheads will in a few years destroy the beach. Documentation is needed to determine how long it will take a given type of structure to reduce the beach size under various conditions of wave energy and sand supply, and how much more rapidly a replenished beach erodes relative to the natural beach it replaced.

Objective long range cost-benefit analyses of alternative management development plans.   At what point does stabilization result in economic loss? Which developed islands, like Coney Island, are worth trying to stabilize? These analyses must take the long range view, 50 to 100 years, difficult as that may be.

Investigation of the feasibility of demolishing seawalls and bulkheads to permit de – New – Jerseyization.   Perhaps by a combination of shorefront building destruction, sea wall removal and extensive beach replenishment, the natural system could be reinstated. As the expenditures rise to build more and more miles of concrete shorelines, while simultaneously increasing loss of beaches, the de–New–Jerseyization alternative would not be as radical as it may seem. The one-time expenditure of demolishing these harmful structures and replenishing the beach will likely be small compared to the long range cost of seawall construction and maintenance. Considerable research is needed on how best to restore islands.

Major applied research in the coming decade should address the gaps in our understanding by increased study of the dynamics of shoreline systems "stabilized" through engineering projects; and by application of geologic principles of shoreline dynamics to coastal zone and island management.

Increased understanding of large scale shoreline processes.   The beach must be studied in the context of its relationship to the entire continental shelf. We also need to expand knowledge of the role beaches play in island evolution and in the regional sand transport system. There is critical need for additional research on the shoreline's catastrophic events, especially storms, to help us avoid the mistakes of the past.

We must recognize the sandy beach shoreline system as a dynamic equilibrium involving sediment supply, wave energy, surface shape, and rising sea levels. Although we understand a great deal about this dynamic equilibrium in the short term, we have only a minimal understanding of this system's longer range workings.

Conclusion

All too often we have failed to view shorefront erosion from a sufficiently broad geological perspective. The beach erosion problem cannot be addressed in the context of the beach alone. It is only the most visible aspect of a larger coastal system, and our mismanagement of these systems has created the current crisis. A "solution" to the beach erosion problem will never be found without considering the complete natural system within a long-term time frame and without applying a principle of minimal human intervention.

These, then, are the breakthrough concepts needed to understand coastal erosion. They comprise a view which looks beyond the next public works program or upcoming election, toward an understanding of the long range impact of the interrelated forces which affect the shore. Implementation of these ideas will shape the way we manage our shoreline and direct our marine studies. It will help us to live in harmony with the coastal ecosystem.

Oil and Fish:
Can They Coexist?

ROBERT W. HOWARTH

ROBERT W. HOWARTH
is an assistant scientist at the Ecosystems Center of the Marine
Biological Laboratory in Woods Hole, Massachusetts. He earned
his PhD in 1979 in a Joint Program in Biological Oceanography
from MIT and the Woods Hole Oceanographic Institute.
His research interests are in several areas: energy flow in anoxic
ecosystems; sulfur biochemistry; coupling of carbon, nitrogen,
and sulfur cycles in salt marshes; microbial production;
physiological ecology of marsh grasses; environmental management; and the effects of pollutants in marine ecosystems. He has
written extensively on these topics in a variety of technical and
scientific journals.

What effect does oil have on marine life? The reply is complex, contradictory, incomplete. The next two essays explore, from different vantage points, partial answers.

In this essay, Robert W. Howarth of the Marine Biological Laboratory outlines the complicated processes by which oil disperses through sea water, and how such oil affects mature fish, fish eggs and larvae. He warns that dramatic oil spills produce only a fraction of the oil that enters the marine environment. Chronic and insidious discharges of oil from tankers, wells, barges, sewage runoff and a dozen other sources may be far more harmful to fisheries.

Dr. Howarth says that just because an oil slick disappears, it does not mean that danger from the oil has also disappeared. Quite the opposite is often true. The components that are the most toxic are also among the most water soluble.

As oil drilling begins on Georges Bank, off New England, Dr. Howarth discusses why it may be a major threat to fisheries there. Comparisons of the Georges Bank area with Gulf Coast fisheries may be invalid. Important fish and shellfish in the Gulf spawn in inshore waters, not offshore, while on Georges Bank a circular current carries floating fish eggs and larvae right through the drilling area.

O IL COMPANY ADVERTISEMENTS show film of schools of fish swimming past an offshore oil drilling rig. The fish appear healthy, the water clear and sparkling. The message is that fishing is as good as ever, the water unpolluted despite oil production operations. Yet wherever and whenever offshore oil and natural gas drilling is proposed, fishermen are among the first to protest vehemently. They fear that their catch will be either contaminated or reduced. Alongside the fishermen, environmentalists fight a dogged battle to prevent — or failing that, at least to limit — oil and gas activities in the most fragile marine ecosystems. The battle tends to be an unequal one, and the pace of offshore oil and gas activities accelerates yearly.

Announcing a speedup in government leases of offshore areas for oil exploration, Secretary of the Interior James Watt in April of 1981 asserted that despite the fact that about 4,000 offshore wells pump oil and gas beyond the old three-mile limit, there have been but two spills of more than 1,000 barrels in the United States since 1970. And, he claimed, spills like the 1969 well blowout off Santa Barbara or the 1979-80 blowout of a Mexican well in the Gulf of Mexico have not caused "significant long-term damage" to the marine environment.

By contrast, only the day before the Watts' announcement Governor Edmund Brown of California had objected strongly to opening four areas off northern California to oil and gas drilling. He stated that potential environmental and economic damage was not worth the amount of oil that might be found in those areas.

How is the public to know where the truth lies in such disputes? Each proposal for increased offshore oil production or expanded coastal petroleum facilities intensifies the debate on the effects of oil on marine life. With more drilling, more pipelines, more tankers, and oil barges, more refining facilities, inevitably more petroleum will enter our coastal water. We need to know with much more certainty how the chronic low-level pollution that is inevitable in such activities will affect or alter the marine ecosystem.

Without solid information, citizens cannot intelligently assess policy decisions on offshore oil proposals, port development plans, tanker safety rules, and other critical issues that relate to oil in fishing waters. How can the dangers to marine life be measured and therefore judged against the value of the petroleum to be gained? What documented evidence can science provide on whether fish and oil can coexist in coastal waters?

Much of the contradiction over whether damage results from oil development stems from the difficulty of proving clear causal relationships in a dynamic, complex ecosystem. There is a growing body of evidence to indicate oil pollution can adversely affect a variety of marine organisms. Yet determining the precise effects of oil pollution on commercial fisheries or other resources our society takes from the sea is scientifically difficult. When the *Amoco Cadiz* ran aground off the Brittany coast of France in March of 1978, spilling 233,000 tons of oil, damage to commercial shellfisheries and finfisheries was both obvious and widespread. Less encompassing damage, or damage which occurs more gradually as a result of chronic pollution, is much more difficult to link causally with petroleum oil pollution.

Scientists are making rapid progress in their understanding of the potential effects of oil on marine life. But the effects of oil can be subtle, the scientific debates complicated. Public debate and policy lag behind scientific understanding. This paper is an attempt to help bridge this gap.

Chronic Pollution/Catastrophic Pollution

Petroleum enters the marine environment either through the chronic discharge of low levels of contamination or as a result of a catastrophic event like the 1976 wreck of the *Argo Merchant* tanker off Nantucket. While a tanker breakup or a wellhead blowout spewing tons of oil into our waters make the headlines, the truth is that such catastrophic pollution is only the most visible part of the problem.

Catastrophic accidents account for only a small proportion of the oil that finds its way into our seas and coastal waters. According to a 1973 National Academy of Sciences panel [18], tanker accidents contribute perhaps two to four percent of the total amount. Likewise, in an average year, offshore oil production probably directly accounts for between one and two percent of all oil introduced to the oceans. A single offshore accident, however, can drastically alter this figure. The spill resulting from the 1979 blowout of a single well (IXTOC 1) in the Gulf of Mexico probably released ten to 50 times more oil than is usually discharged from all offshore oil operations in an average year, according to the estimates of MIT's Professor Jerry Milgram [16].

While it is estimated that more than *six million metric tons* of oil are released to the world's oceans every year, we do not know if this amount is increasing, remaining constant, or decreasing. We *do* know much more oil enters the oceans now than 20 years ago when the world used less oil; more now than even during World War II when tankers were frequently sunk.

Most of this oil, more than 90 percent yearly, enters the marine environment through mundane — and thus scarcely visible — sources. Chronic contamination comes from small amounts of oil released on a continuing basis — in sewage effluents, stormwater runoff in urban centers, discharges from oil refineries, intentional discharges from offshore oil rigs, industrial releases, and in routine discharges and leaks of oil associated with transporting oil by tanker and barge.

Recent estimates by Professor Jim Butler of Harvard [4] suggest that perhaps one-third of all the oil which enters the oceans is the result of these routine tanker discharges. Other chronic sources are the rainout of pollutant hydrocarbons from the atmosphere and street runoff. The original sources of these pollutants include unburned compounds in vehicular exhaust — particularly from diesel engines — and evaporative losses from filling stations, etc.

Chronic inputs of oil are less dramatic and more diffuse than the occasional accidental spill and so usually escape the attention of the press and the public. However, chronic inputs can have serious effects on coastal areas. Over time, low-level inputs can accumulate in sediments. Even low concentrations of oil in water can disrupt marine ecosystems. The effects of continuous low-level discharges can be as severe as those of spills, perhaps more severe.

The kind of chronic, insidious oil pollution I am describing occurs most often in coastal waters rather than in areas far from shore. Similarly oil spills from tanker or barge breakups happen most often in waters closest to shore. Thus both chronic and catastrophic pollution are greatest in the very areas that have the greatest biological productivity, the waters from which commercial fisheries and sports fishermen harvest the largest catch, the areas in which most fish spawn and in which shellfish can live. As more oil seeps into these waters annually, what happens to fish and shellfish? In what ways does petroleum change the ecosystem in which fish and shellfish live and reproduce?

Oil in Seawater: What Happens Next?

Our understanding of the behavior of oil in seawater and its effects on the marine environment is far from complete. Most of our knowledge has come only in the last decade or so. However, it is known that oil is toxic to a variety of organisms at very low concentrations. Oil spills can seriously disrupt marine ecosystems, and the effects of such disruptions can be long-lasting. After an oil spill, oil can persist for years — or decades — in marine sediments.

To begin to understand the biological effects of oil, it is necessary to know something about the composition of oil and its chemical and physical behavior in seawater. Oils are complex mixtures of thousands of different organic compounds. Despite more than thirty years of effort, chemists are still unable to separate and characterize all of these compounds. Most of the compounds which make up an oil are called hydrocarbons, that is, they consist of carbon and hydrogen atoms. Some constituent compounds of oil also contain oxygen, nitrogen, or sulfur. Hydrocarbons are only very slightly soluble in water, and oils are less dense than water. Consequently, when oil is spilled, it tends to form a slick on the surface.

A variety of processes act on an oil slick that cause it to disappear gradually. These processes include evaporation; mixing or dissolution into the underlying water; degradation by chemical or biological means; adsorption to particles in the water; or incorporation into the fecal pellets of tiny animals which may feed on drops of oil. All of these processes make the oil less noticeable to the human eye. However, they may not be making the oil any less harmful.

After an oil spill public attention is usually focused on the slick. When the slick disappears, many people assume that the deleterious effects of oil have also dissipated. With oil, "out of sight, out of mind" reasoning is wrong. For example, the use of chemical dispersants to speed the disappearance of a slick may in fact increase harmful effects by solubilizing the oil in the water and therefore making it more likely to come in contact with marine animals in the water column.

Evaporation

Until fairly recently it was believed widely that evaporation of oil to the atmosphere was the major process causing a slick to break up. Actual studies in controlled artificial ecosystems, such as those used in the Marine Ecosystems Research Laboratory (MERL) studies at the University of Rhode Island have challenged this assumption.

The MERL studies use artificial ecosystems consisting of large tanks of seawater with muddy sediment at the bottom. The artificial systems are designed to mimic the natural ecosystems of a coastal bay. They contain the same sorts of animals and plants, but since the tanks are confined and can be more easily sampled, the fate of oil added to these "marine ecosystems" can be measured more readily.

There is less evaporative loss of oil from these systems than had been expected. Evaporative loss was most significant during the summer, much smaller during the winter. While the diminished wave action in these controlled systems, in comparison to wave action in open waters, may have decreased evaporation, these findings suggest that evaporation may be much more important in warm southern waters than in cold northern seas.

Although evaporation helps to disperse an oil slick, the oil hydrocarbons are not lost from the environment. These chemicals are merely transferred to the atmosphere, from which they may later be rained back into the ocean. While in the atmosphere, these oil hydrocarbons may undergo chemical change. As discussed below, their toxicity may actually increase.

Weathering

Another process acting to disperse an oil slick is the dissolution of the more readily dissolved compounds into the water. Even though the solubility of most petroleum compounds in water is quite low, they will dissolve eventually because of the large volume of water available. Since some compounds which make up an oil are more water soluble than others, the water will be enriched with these chemicals. Unfortunately, the most water-soluble compounds also tend to be the most toxic. In part this may be because once dissolved in water, such chemicals are more available for uptake by organisms.

Oil can also be mixed into water as suspended drops. A range of mixtures of oil and water can occur, depending on the type of oil and weather conditions. Some mixtures are mostly water while others are predominantly oil. Waves increase the extent of this phenomenon, and a storm can drive oil drops as deep as 80 meters into the water column. This mixing significantly increases the rate of oil dissolution into the water as it increases the surface area of exposed oil.

Bottom Contamination

Some species of zooplankton — the tiny, free-floating animals of the sea — are known to feed on particles of oil. The oil they consume collects in their fecal pellets, and as the fecal pellets sink to the bottom, the oil sinks with them. As a result of his studies of this process, Dr. C. Parker calculated that a typical population of zooplankton (two individuals per liter) grazing on an oil slick could transport three tons of oil per square kilometer daily to the bottom sediments [20]. It is well to pause for a moment over that figure, for it shows how quickly and massively oil collects on the bottom.

Another mechanism whereby oil can be transported to the bottom is the adsorption of oil hydrocarbons to particles suspended in the water column. Oil itself is lighter than water and will float, but oil-sediment combinations are heavier than water and sink to the bottom. The number of studies where scientists have looked for oil in bottom sediments after a spill is somewhat limited, but most attempts to examine this process have found that oil is transported rapidly to the bottom. Controlled experiments with the MERL artificial ecosystems, mentioned earlier, also showed a significant transport of oil to the bottom sediments.

Chronic, low-level discharges of oil are a significant case of bottom contamination. Even in the absence of major oil spills, studies have shown sediment contamination around offshore oil platforms. Equally disturbing, sediments near urban centers which have been studied are highly contaminated with oil hydrocarbons. The work of Dr. John Farrington and his colleagues at the Woods Hole Oceanographic Institution [6, 7] has shown surface sediments just offshore from the Statue of Liberty in New York to be about 0.1% oil (dry weight basis). Most of this oil is probably associated with sewage sludge and contaminated dredge spoils.

Oil in Water: The Toxic Problem

Petroleum can be degraded by chemical processes and by the action of bacteria. In nature, degradation can be a very slow process. Studies have shown that after an oil spill, oil hydrocarbons can persist in the sediments for years or decades. Some hydrocarbons are produced by living organisms, so it is not surprising that organisms are also able to decompose hydrocarbons. But, in several ways, the hydrocarbons produced by living organisms differ from those found in oil.

Oils contain a much more complex mix of hydrocarbons as well as a class of hydrocarbons called aromatics. They include the most water soluble, environmentally persistent, and toxic compounds found in oil. Some of the aromatics present in petroleum are carcinogenic. Aromatics are not found in uncontaminated organisms.

Differences between hydrocarbons in living organisms and those in oils may seem paradoxical since oils are derived originally from biologically produced materials. These materials have undergone geochemical changes over very long periods of time at high pressures and temperatures. In this process, the vast new array of hydrocarbons is produced.

A common assumption of a decade ago was that as oil "weathered" — as it was acted upon by the processes of evaporation, dissolution, degradation, etc. — it became less toxic. Research in the last few years has cast doubt on this assumption. In many cases, the decomposition of oil hydrocarbons can result in new, more toxic substances containing oxygen atoms as well as atoms of carbon and hydrogen. Some of these new substances are potentially carcinogenic as well. Many are more water soluble than the parent hydrocarbons. Consequently, although processes that degrade the oil speed the disappearance of an oil slick, they may increase the concentration of toxic and carcinogenic compounds dissolved in seawater.

Killer Doses and "Sub-lethal Effects"

A number of studies have indicated that dissolved oil can be toxic at very low concentrations. Concentrations as low as ten parts of oil compounds dissolved in a billion parts of water have been shown to cause death in some organisms. Concentrations of the water soluble fractions of oil in the range of 0.2 to one part per billion have been shown to be detrimental to certain life processes in a variety of marine animals, plants, and bacteria. Recent studies have shown that the concentrations found in many coastal areas near urban or industrial centers are in this damaging range. Concentrations of oil hydrocarbons below the slick from the *Argo Merchant* spill off the coast of New England were as high as 250 parts per billion.

The scientific literature on laboratory studies of oil toxicity is immense. Yet many of these studies are of little use in accurately predicting the effects of oil on natural systems such as coastal waters. A major problem of these toxicity studies is our lack of knowledge about the actual concentration of oil hydrocarbons to which an organism has been exposed. In many studies, this concentration was probably less than was assumed. Too often, it is not measured.

Many toxicity studies have focused only on those organisms killed by oil, not those that experienced sub-lethal effects. These studies have attempted only to determine the "lethal dose," or the concentration of oil that will kill 50 percent of the individual organisms studied. These are often called LD-50 studies. Such an approach can be quite misleading since sub-lethal effects can occur at concentrations of oil far lower than those necessary to cause death. Although sub-lethal effects can be enormously damaging, they are much more difficult to study in natural systems such as coastal waters.

Some evidence is in, however. Researchers have shown that low concentrations of oil inhibit the growth of various types of phytoplankton, the microscopic plants of the ocean. Similarly, low concentrations of oil reduce the reproduction of some marine animals and interfere with feeding behavior and communication between animals. In most investigations of these sub-lethal effects of oil, the damage has occurred even at the lowest concentrations of oil examined.

Some types of organisms are much more tolerant to pollution and stress than are others. Ecologists call such organisms "opportunists" because they can readily take advantage of the opportunity to grow and reproduce when stressful situations eliminate most other species. Toxicity studies often use opportunistic species because they are much easier to grow under stressful laboratory conditions. However, it should be obvious that studies which use opportunists will not reflect the possible harm which oil pollution may pose to less resilient species.

Organisms are often more sensitive to the effects of oil at one point in their life cycle than at another. Adult fish, for example, apparently are fairly tolerant of oil. Fish eggs and the young larvae of fish, on the other hand, are easily poisoned by very low oil concentrations. Many toxicity studies fail to take life histories into account.

Another potential flaw in many early oil toxicity studies has been recognized only in the last few years. As noted previously, toxicity can increase as oil degrades. Many oils undergo rapid oxidation when exposed to the type of strong ultraviolet light found in sunlight at the ocean surface. This photo-oxidative degradation of oil has been shown specifically to increase the toxicity of the oil. Yet almost all laboratory toxicity studies have been carried out under artificial light, which contains considerably less ultraviolet light than sunlight (it is very difficult to get a tan in the average research laboratory). Consequently, under laboratory conditions, less photo-oxidation of hydrocarbons into more toxic substances takes place than would occur when a real oil slick is exposed to sunlight. Therefore the lab studies may greatly underestimate the potential toxicity of the oil. Dramatic evidence of this was obtained by Dr. Richard Larson and his colleagues at the Philadelphia Academy of Sciences [12]. They found that just one day of exposure to a strong ultraviolet light source approximating that found in nature increased the toxicity of an oil to yeasts by four-fold.

Many representatives of the oil industry have tried to persuade the public that although refined oil products such as home heating oils can have toxic effects, crude oils, oils as they come out of the ground, are relatively non-toxic. As an example, during a public meeting in New England designed to defuse fears about offshore oil development, a representative of Texaco's Environmental Protection Division was quoted as saying that "the oil found on the Georges Bank would be crude oil which is not dangerous" [7]. This position is unfounded. Refined oils are derived from crude oils, and the same toxic components found in the refined oils are also found in the crudes. It is true that the percentage of toxic substances in the oil is higher for many types of refined oils than for crude oils. The percentage of toxic substances in the oil varies among crude oils from different fields and regions, but the toxic components are still present.

Regardless of the type of oil, the components which dissolve into the water tend to be the most toxic. There is no evidence to support the assertion that dissolved oil compounds below a slick from a crude oil spill are less concentrated than dissolved oil compounds from a refined oil spill. The *Amoco Cadiz* carried crude oil, and the spill had wide-spread, massive toxic effects.

Oil and Fisheries: How Volatile the Mix?

If there is oil in the water, and that oil is toxic, even if invisible, what effects can oil have on a commercial fishery? Perhaps the most obvious is contamination of fish with oil. Since oil hydrocarbons are more soluble in tissues than in water, these compounds tend to accumulate in marine organisms, including commercially important fish and shellfish. Gilled aquatic animals pass tremendous amounts of water over their gills. These organs are designed to facilitate the transfer of substances between the organism and the water. Contaminant hydrocarbons can be absorbed from or lost to the water through the gills. Since these petroleum hydrocarbons tend to lodge in fatty tissues, an individual fish may contain significantly more contamination than is found in the water.

Shellfish Contamination

Fish and shellfish which are contaminated with oil hydrocarbons pose a public health hazard because some of the contaminant hydrocarbons are carcinogenic. In severe cases, contaminated fish and shellfish actually taste of oil, but the lack of such a taste does not guarantee an absence of contamination. Contamination of shellfish with oil components often leads — or should lead — to the closing of commercially valuable fisheries. After a small spill off Cape Cod, Massachusetts, described elsewhere in this volume, portions of the shellfish beds were contaminated with oil and closed to harvesting for more than ten years.

Shellfish contamination is a major and widespread problem along the coast, as indicated by the results of the "Mussel Watch" program. Mussel Watch is a nation-wide research project involving several universities and research laboratories. Mussels from various locations are periodically analyzed for a variety of pollutants, including oil hydrocarbons. The results of this program indicate that mussels taken near major urban areas are chronically contaminated with carcinogenic and toxic substances, some of which are derived from oils.

Life Cycles and Fish Mortality

While it is easy enough to document examples of shellfish killed by oil pollution, documented evidence of adult finfish killed by oil pollution is rather rare. That does not mean that oil pollution cannot kill fish. As noted earlier, fish eggs and fish larvae are more sensitive to the toxic effects of oil than adult fish. A Russian scientist, Dr. Oleg Miranov, has demonstrated that concentrations as low as ten parts in a billion parts of water can cause death among a significant percentage of fish eggs [17]. Very few attempts have been made to look for the death of fish eggs or larvae from exposure to oil pollution in nature. Since the fish eggs and larvae are very tiny, their death can be easily overlooked.

Extremely disturbing findings on the effects of oil on fish eggs and larvae came in a study following the 1976 *Argo Merchant* spill off the New England coast by Dr. Arlene Crosby-Longwell, a scientist from the National Marine Fisheries Service [14]. Dr. Longwell found that a high percentage of fish eggs sampled underneath the oil slick or at stations near the slick were contaminated with drops of oil sticking to them. Averaged over the stations she sampled, about 20 percent of cod eggs and 46 percent of pollock eggs were either dead or gave the appearance of dying. Dr. Longwell has examined mackerel eggs in the chronically polluted waters of the New York Bight off New York City and has found poor egg survival in most areas sampled. Oil pollution may or may not have been a contributing factor.

An earlier study, after the *Torrey Canyon* spill off Lands End, England, in 1967, also reported a significant fish egg mortality. Some 50 to 90 percent of the eggs of the pilchard were affected. However, in the *Torrey Canyon* study, it was not known if this high mortality resulted from toxic effects of the oil, dispersants used to "clean up" the spill, or from some unknown factor.

While such results are disturbing, we do not know enough about the basic biological controls on fish populations to determine exactly how serious these fish egg mortalities are. The variability in fish populations from year to year is very large. Production of new young fish of a particular species is low most years, and very high in occasional years. New fish produced in any given year are called an age class. High production of new young fish is called a strong age class. In years after a strong age class occurs, adult fish are generally more abundant. In fact, most of the commercial fish catch consists of these strong age classes. Factors which cause these occasional strong age classes are not well known and may vary from species to species and region to region.

An adult female fish produces a tremendous number of eggs each year; most of them die. Does the mortality of fish eggs caused by oil pollution increase total mortality of fish eggs and larvae, and therefore decrease the resulting number of adult fish? Or when oil kills some fish eggs or larvae, do the remaining ones have a higher chance of living (density dependent mortality, in the language of an ecologist)? We do not know for sure, and the answer may vary among fisheries. In any event it is very likely that any additional source of mortality of fish eggs and larvae will cause at least some decrease in age class size.

Subtle Ecosystem Shifts

In addition to the possible direct effects on fish, oil may have indirect effects by causing subtle changes in the ecosystem supporting a fishery. One such change is a shift in the types of phytoplankton, or microscopic plant life found in a water body. Recent experiments with artificial ecosystems, consisting of large plastic bags suspended in a fjord in British Columbia (the CEPEX experiments) have demonstrated that a variety of low level pollutants can cause the replacement of relatively large species of phytoplankton by much smaller species. In the artificial ecosystem, oil concentrations as low as 20 parts per billion had this effect. Similar replacement also occurred temporarily after the *Torrey Canyon* spill. A similar change appears to be occurring in the North Sea, perhaps due in part to chronic oil pollution from tanker traffic and coastal industries [8].

Is such a change in the phytoplankton community significant? Dr. W. Greve of Germany and Dr. T. R. Parsons of Canada convincingly argued in a 1977 paper that such a shift might induce a change in the type of animals found further up the food chain and thus lead to replacement of the top carnivores in the ecosystem [9]. In practical terms that means that important fish might be replaced by jellyfish-like animals (ctenophores, salps, etc.), which are at present of no direct use to humans. Thus, a subtle, sub-lethal growth inhibition of some phytoplankton species by low concentrations of oil might ultimately reduce dramatically the fish catch of commercial fisheries.

Another potential but subtle threat oil pollution poses to commerical fisheries is its effect on bottom-dwelling animals. A number of studies have shown that oil can seriously disturb the community of animals that inhabits the bottom sediments. Many commercially important fish feed on bottom animals for much of their food. Therefore a change in the composition of these animal communities can potentially affect a fishery.

One of the earliest and best studies on the effect of an oil spill on the bottom community was conducted by Howard Sanders and his colleagues at the Woods Hole Oceanographic Institution following a small spill in West Falmouth, Massachusetts, in 1969 [25] as discussed by Dr. Sanders and Carol Jones elsewhere in this volume. The massive kill following the spill left some areas of sediment completely devoid of animal life. At first, these areas were repopulated by only one species of worm, *Capitella capitata*. This pollutant-tolerant, opportunistic species is common in polluted harbor sediments and is one of the very few species of animals which has been able to survive and reproduce in the oil-contaminated sediments near an oil refinery in Los Angeles Harbor.

Recovery Succession After Oil Spills

The process of species recovery at West Falmouth can perhaps best be understood by analogy to terrestrial succession. When a fire burns down a forest, opportunistic species, grasses and shrubs, appear almost immediately. But for the forest to recover its original state is a process which takes decades. Similarly, at West Falmouth the bottom community had not fully recovered its original state six years after the spill. A 1973 study by Dr. Wheeler North of the 1957 *Tampico Maru* spill showed that the recovery of some affected rocky areas may not have been complete even after 16 years [19]. As of 1973, mussels and green abalone had not yet repopulated some of the regions.

While it is possible to construct a careful scientific study of the toxic results of a localized oil spill, it is much more difficult for scientists to study the precise effects of the more diffused, chronic oil pollution discussed earlier. Yet such pollution may be a much greater threat to fisheries than the more dramatic occasional spills.

Oil industry representatives repeatedly cite evidence from the Gulf of Mexico, where oil production began more than three decades ago, to prove that oil operations do not harm fisheries. A major study of the effect of oil on marine life in the Gulf is discussed — and discounted — by Dr. Sanders later in this volume. As the toxicity studies just cited show, much more research on fish and oil is required before anybody can reach scientifically valid conclusions about the effect of oil on fisheries.

The Gulf Coast and Georges Banks: How Comparable?

Oil has been flowing from offshore wells in the Gulf of Mexico for more than 35 years. Even without oil spills or well blowouts, oil production produces chronic low-level pollution of water and bottom sediments. If oil pollution can damage a fishery, then perhaps we should see such damage in the Gulf. Although oil industry representatives imply that the fisheries of the Gulf of Mexico are in fine health, in fact they have developed several unhealthy signs. It is true that fish catches have remained steady for years in the Gulf. However, in more recent years much more effort and energy have been required to catch the same volume of fish. For instance, according to a 1975 report of the National Academy of Sciences [18], average daily shrimp catch per boat dropped from almost 14 tons per day in 1950 to just three tons per day in 1972. Oyster harvest per area of grounds fished dropped steadily from 560 kilograms per hectare in 1945 to 64 kilograms per hectare in 1972.

Oil pollution may or may not be partially responsible for the diminished catches. In hindsight, without careful scientific studies conducted over the time the fisheries developed these unhealthy signs, there is virtually no way to know. Other possible causes of smaller catches may be different forms of pollution, overfishing, some unknown natural fluctuation, or the destruction and alteration of marshlands. This last reason is perhaps the most likely, for oil development has been a major cause of marshland destruction along the Gulf shore. More marshland has probably been destroyed by opening canals for oil barges than by direct oil pollution.

Despite various lines of evidence that Gulf fisheries have been disturbed by oil operations, the abundance of marine life in the oil-producing Gulf region is used by oil spokesmen to argue that oil activities would do no damage elsewhere, notably in the productive fishing waters of Georges Banks.

Georges Bank: Treacherous, Productive

Georges Bank, one of the world's most productive fisheries, is now slated for offshore oil exploration. Despite vehement objections, and a three year court fight by environmentalists and fishermen, drilling was scheduled to begin in summer of 1981 at Georges Bank. Lying some 150-250 miles offshore of New England, Georges Bank is a relatively unpolluted portion of the continental shelf. Strong tides and oceanic waves interact on shoals only ten feet beneath the ocean's surface in some locations to make it a very treacherous piece of water. Despite the navigational hazards, Georges Bank has attracted fishermen for more than 400 years. It was this marvelously productive fishery which attracted large foreign fishing fleets to American waters in the 1960's and 1970's, creating the pressure which led to the expansion of our territorial boundary from three to 200 miles offshore.

At its peak in the early 1970's, the fish catch at Georges Bank was the highest per unit area for any major fishery in the world. Regulation to control overfishing has reduced the catch significantly, but Georges Bank is still one of the most productive fisheries in the world. By comparison, fisheries in the Gulf of Mexico are much more diffuse, with the average catch per unit area perhaps ten-fold less.

The reasons for the tremendous productivity of fish on Georges Bank are still not completely clear. But phytoplankton production — which is at the base of the food chain — is among the highest measured for any oceanic region. The dominant species of phytoplankton are large in size, which allows for short food chains and efficient passage of energy to the fish.

We cannot rigorously predict how oil development will affect the Georges Bank fishery. There is too much uncertainty. We know too little about the basic biological controls on the fishery and about the way oil will affect those controls. However, we can create potential scenarios based on the knowledge we now have.

According to government estimates, a rather small oil find is expected, perhaps a little more than 120 million barrels from the leases sold so far (lease sale #42). Although that may sound like a great deal of oil, it would be a very small field. To put the figure in perspective, if that amount of oil were developed and used at one time, it would supply the country's use for only three to four days. If the field proves to be small, considering its distance from shore, Georges will be only marginally economical, relative to other fields.

Consequently, if the field is developed, we might expect to see the use of cheaper technology which would cause a higher percentage of oil to be discharged into the seawater. Because it is so far offshore, tankers rather than pipelines will be used to transport oil ashore. Unless special tankers are used, we might expect the chronic release of oil to be quite high. The Department of Interior estimates that perhaps 0.4 percent of the oil pumped at Georges might be discharged or spilled. Most of that would be in chronic small spills and in routine, legally allowed discharges associated with loading tankers. In January, 1981 the Coast Guard took steps to limit discharges by requiring that oil from offshore development be carried in segregated ballast tankers. However, much more needs to be done.

The Gyre at Georges

Although not confined by any land masses, Georges Bank is a distinct body of water defined by a semi-closed circular current pattern, or gyre. Within the gyre, water moves clockwise in a revolution that takes about three months to circle the Bank. The eggs and larvae of most of the commercially important fish on Georges are buoyant and float passively for four to five months while they develop into juvenile fish, which can swim. During this time, eggs and larvae float in the gyre, for an average of 1.5 revolutions around the Bank. Consequently, most fish eggs and larvae during this highly sensitive stage of their life will ride the moving water through areas where oil is being drilled. There they will be exposed to chronically polluted waters which may have concentrations of oil enough to cause a significant mortality.

Some government officials have argued that the fisheries of Georges will be adequately protected merely by prohibiting oil development in the spawning grounds. While such protection is important, it is hardly sufficient to protect the area where the fish are laid. All of Georges Bank is a nursery for the fish. Because of the gyre, it should be protected as a unit.

The Biological Difference

Those who would extrapolate from the Gulf of Mexico to Georges Bank would be well advised to study the basic biological differences between the fisheries. As noted earlier, adult fish are relatively insensitive to oil's toxic effects. Fish eggs and larvae, on the other hand, are vulnerable and deserve special protection. On Georges Bank, fish eggs and larvae develop offshore on the Bank itself. For most of the species found there (e.g. cod, pollock, haddock, whiting, hake, cusp, dab, flounder, sole and scallops), eggs and larvae are buoyant and tend to float near the surface where exposure to high concentrations of oil is most likely.

By contrast, the life histories of the commercially important fish and shellfish of the Gulf of Mexico, are very different. The larvae of all the important species (menhaden, oysters, and shrimp) develop in the wetlands and estuaries ashore, and not in the waters offshore. Thus, in the Gulf Coast, areas in most urgent need of protection are the marshes and estuaries. Oil spills offshore in the Gulf probably are less likely to damage a fishery than would a similar spill on Georges Bank. Menhaden eggs in the Gulf of Mexico do float at the surface, but only for a couple of days. They then develop into larvae which move up into the estuaries. On Georges Bank, eggs and larvae typically float in a vulnerable stage for four to five months.

The gyre on Georges Bank is tighter some years than others. That is, some years more water is exchanged off the Bank than others. Two scientists of the National Marine Fisheries Service, Drs. John Colton and Robert Temple, suggested in a 1961 paper that the age classes of fish on Georges are tied to the integrity of the gyre [5]. Their hypothesis, which seems reasonable, is that in years when the gyre is tight, fish eggs and larvae are held within the highly productive waters, and a good age class results from their relatively high survival rate. In years when the gyre is less tight, more water is exchanged off the Bank, carrying with it more floating fish eggs and larvae into the less productive waters where fewer survive.

If this hypothesis is correct, then the same conditions which would normally lead to a large age class, i.e., a tight gyre, might also be expected to cause an accumulation of oil from chronic discharges. Such an accumulation might kill large numbers of eggs and larvae. The net result over a period of years might be a series of average or mediocre age classes, with oil pollution causing a decrease in the year-to-year variability. While commercial fisheries would suffer, it would be very difficult scientifically to detect or attribute the problem to oil.

How Valuable Are the Fisheries?

How does one compare the worth of a fishery with the value of oil? One year's fish catch on Georges Bank, in terms of the landed value, more or less equals the value of the oil that is expected to result from the leases thus far sold (lease sale #42), although different studies indicate that one or the other of the two industries is worth more. Regardless of the value of the oil, the oil industry and government have argued that we should develop this area since every little bit of petroleum counts. Perhaps we can best assess this argument by comparing the energy value of the oil with the energy cost of replacing the fishery.

Much of the food produced in the United States is produced at a very high energy cost. For instance, it takes 26.2 gallons of oil to produce one kilogram of beef protein, 8.7 gallons of oil to produce one kilogram of milk protein. By comparison, New England fisheries are a very efficient food producing system. On average, only 0.53 gallons of oil are needed to produce (catch) one kilogram of fish protein, even including such costs as the energy needed to build the fishing boats [22, 24].

Suppose we were to pursue the "Texas alternative" of drilling for oil on Georges Bank and replacing with beef any protein lost because of damage to the fishery? Because the energy costs of pro-ducing beef are so much greater than are the costs of landing fish from Georges Bank, replacing the fish protein could cost a lot of energy. At the peak of the fishery in the early 1970's, 1.8 billion pounds of fish were caught on Georges every year, the equivalent of 70 billion grams of protein annually. To replace this with beef protein would cost 42 million barrels of oil per year, almost seven times more oil than is expected to be produced from the present lease sale every year. We should also note that the Georges Bank oil field is expected to last for only 20 years.

Oil development will not completely wipe out the fish of Georges Bank, but a significant reduction in catch is possible even with stringent safeguards. This analysis shows that the net energy gained by society may not be that much. In fact, as we develop more and more marginal oil fields we run a risk of gaining less energy than we lose.

To protect a fishery such as Georges Bank, some measures are certainly worth taking. For example, a major potential source of oil pollution on Georges Bank was estimated to be chronic releases from tankers washing their tanks. A normal tanker carries oil in its tanks on one leg of a voyage, and after unloading, fills its tanks with water to gain stability for the return voyage. Before oil is reloaded, this water and its oil contaminants must be dumped.

Such discharges on Georges Bank can be avoided by using seg-regated ballast tankers, that is, tankers with two separate types of tanks. One set of tanks carries oil to port, and another set of tanks is filled with water for the return voyage. Oil and water are never mixed. Tankers such as these, although not common, are at pres-ent in use. According to a 1978 paper in the *New Scientist* [13] the use of such tankers might increase the cost of oil by 0.5-0.6 cents per gallon. This cost is clearly justified, and the Coast Guard, as of January 1981, has required the use of such tankers on Georges Bank.

If oil production proceeds, the means of reducing other pollu-tion sources may be more expensive. For example, during oil exploration and development, drilling muds containing many toxic constituents are routinely dumped from rigs. These muds can be barged ashore, but the cost can be high. Beth Mullin of Yale University has estimated that barging costs at Georges Bank could be as high as all other drilling costs combined. Current regulations call for the best available, economically feasible technology for minimizing pollution. Is it economically feasible to double the costs of drilling a well by requiring that contaminated muds be barged ashore? Perhaps so, when compared with the value of the fishery or the potential profit from a well.

What can be done to minimize the harmful effects of oil pollution? A first step is to recognize that oil spill clean-up operations are not the answer. As we have noted, accidental spills are only a small part of the problem, introducing probably only two to four percent of the total oil that finds its way into the oceans. When clean-up efforts are made, they do not succeed in removing more than a fraction of the spilled oil. Even from protected waters, less than 25 percent of spilled oil has been recovered, according to Dr. Robert Stewart of the National Oceanic and Atmospheric Administration. Present clean-up technology is largely ineffective when waves are greater than six feet, when winds are greater than 20 knots, when currents are greater than 1-2 knots, or when ice is present. Thus to rely on clean-up after a spill is not to solve the problem.

More importantly, clean-ups after spills have no effect on the far more pervasive — but largely invisible — day-to-day oil contamination from wells, production platforms, tankers, refineries, barges, sewage run-off and dozens of other sources of oil in our fishing waters.

From both an economic and ecological perspective, the best way to reduce oil's impact on the marine environment is to minimize the input of petroleum hydrocarbons into the sea. An obvious first step is to reduce the chronic petroleum discharges which contribute such a large share of the oil in the ocean. We are beginning to make progress in this direction through such steps as requiring segregated ballast tankers. However, we need to do much more. Some oil is moved by barge rather than tanker, and barges remain virtually unregulated. Routine discharges of petroleum-contaminated waters from offshore rigs and oil refineries should be further restricted. And we need to restrict non-point discharges of hydrocarbons such as those emitted by vehicles, which, after entering the atmosphere, are rained into the sea.

Because the world's oil reserves are limited, our society will probably be forced to shift to non-petroleum energy sources in the next decades. Unfortunately, the problems of hydrocarbon pollution may not end with the demise of our oil-based economy. For instance, pollutant hydrocarbons are released into the atmosphere when coal is burned, and much of this pollution can end up in the oceans. In fact, recent work has indicated that a significant percentage of the hydrocarbon pollution in coastal sediments may result from coal burning. If Western coal is shipped to urban areas in pipes as water slurries, new problems may result from disposal of the hydrocarbon-polluted water at the end of the pipelines.

Our society urgently needs to address such problems before we become locked into new facilities built with little regard for environmental pollution. We need also to address other basic questions. Should polluting industries be spread out along our coasts, or should they be concentrated in already environmentally degraded areas to protect the biological resources of more pristine regions? As cheap energy becomes scarcer, natural biological systems with low energy costs, such as fisheries, will become increasingly valuable. We must recognize their value and take steps today to protect them. Such protection is vital for the fragile coastal ecosystems.

Acknowledgements

A condensed version of this paper appeared in *Technology Review*, 83: 68-77. I am grateful to a number of my colleagues for encouraging me in my work on oil pollution. Among these are Drs. Michael Connor, John Farrington, Fred Grassle, John Hobbie, Cindy Lee, Bruce Peterson, Howard Sanders, John Teal, and George Woodwell. Drs. Farrington, Hobbie, Lee, and Peterson reviewed an early draft of this manuscript. Financial assistance was provided by a grant from the Ford Foundation to the Marine Biological Laboratory.

Oil, Science, and Public Policy

HOWARD L. SANDERS
and
CAROL JONES

HOWARD L. SANDERS
is Senior Scientist in Biology at the Woods Hole Oceanographic
Institution. He has been an Associate in Invertebrate Zoology at
Harvard University, a Research Affiliate of the Marine Sciences
Research Center at the State University of New York at Stony
Brook, a correspondent of the Museum National d'Histoire
Naturale, a Fellow of the American Association for the Advance-
ment of Science, and Chairman of the Working Group on Benthic
Productivity of the National Academy of Sciences' Committee
on Oceanography.

CAROL CHARLOTTE JONES
is Assistant Professor of Geology at New England College. She
earned her PhD in Geology from Harvard in 1976. At the Woods
Hole Oceanographic Institute she worked with Dr. Sanders on
the writing up of the research on the West Falmouth oil spill. Her
specialties are clams, dead or alive, and less than 100,000 years old.
She has expertise in the comparative anatomy of Venerid Clams,
Invertebrate Paleontology, and Cenozoic Stratigraphy.

Immediately after an oil barge ran aground in 1969 off West Falmouth, Massachusetts, spilling oil only a few miles from the Woods Hole Oceanographic Institution, Dr. Howard Sanders and his colleagues began a painstaking, long-term study of the effects of the longest biography of an oil spill ever produced. Even before it was published, Sanders' work was severely attacked by the oil industry.

Knowledge gained through the years of their study inspired Dr. Sanders and his colleagues to question the findings of studies which purport to show that oil did no great damage to marine life, particularly to bottom-dwelling life.

In this essay, Dr. Sanders, Senior Scientist in Biology at Woods Hole, and Carol Jones, Assistant Professor of Geology at New England College, discuss the Woods Hole study as well as several widely-circulated reports funded by the oil industry. The scientists reveal serious flaws and distortions in these reports. In the process, they raise a fundamental issue: Privately funded scientific research, on which so many public policy decisions are based, often lacks public accountability. Their essay arouses deep concern about how the integrity of the scientific process can be guaranteed.

T HE SMALL SEGMENT of society trained in basic scientific thinking, must apply its talents to solving a host of rapidly burgeoning crises, from drastic reduction in the quality of life to the very survival of our species [37].* One such crisis is pollution and environmental degradation. The *Florida* oil spill off West Falmouth, Massachusetts, nearly at the doorstep of the Woods Hole Oceanographic Institution, permitted us to undertake a rigorous, detailed determination of the effects of this rather small oil spill on the local marine environment. Our initiative, in turn, set off a train of events that provides a rare glimpse into the never-never land of relevant research and public policy. Some aspects of that insight are: the awesome presence of powerful vested interests; the near absence of checks and balances necessary to decision-making in any viable democratic society; the alarming prolifera-

---

*The numbers in brackets refer to references listed in the Reference section in the back of the book, under the heading "Oil, Science, and Public Policy" p. 170.

tion of 'grey' literature, which circumvents the critical peer review that science traditionally demands to protect its integrity; the uncritical acceptance of such 'grey' literature, often self-serving, as a basis for public policy; and a government that appears either unwilling, unable, or incapable of correcting these abuses. In this essay, you will join us on an odyssey to discover how we gained our insight.

The Florida or West Falmouth Oil Spill

Early in the morning of September 16, 1969, the barge *Florida* ran aground off West Falmouth, Massachusetts, and spilled 650,000 to 700,000 liters of #2 fuel oil into Buzzards Bay. It was serendipitous that the Woods Hole Oceanographic Institution is just a few miles south of the site of the spill, and that we had the freedom, competence, and interest to assemble and interpret data, starting soon after the oil poured into the water.

Strong winds churned this oil into an oil-water emulsion and drove it northeastward into Wild Harbor River. Oil initially spread over an area of more than 1,000 acres, along four miles of coastline. All benthic animals, such as clams, crustaceans, and worms, as well as fish and plants, suffered extremely high mortalities immediately after the spill. Within twelve hours animals began to die in great numbers. Eight to ten days later, soft tissues of dead invertebrates and vertebrates had completely decomposed; any skeletons were soon disarticulated and scattered. Sediments became unstable, marsh grasses died.

We sampled monthly or bimonthly at intertidal and subtidal stations all along a gradient from places in which concentrations of oil were high to those in which they were quite low. We established control stations in unoiled Sippewissett Marsh. This program of sampling enabled us to study the effects of oil on marine life for three to four years.

Aliquots for chemical analysis were subsampled from the biological samples. Blumer and Sass [3] used gas chromatography and mass spectrometry to analyze and identify the #2 fuel oil from the *Florida* spill and to measure degradation of its various components over a period of years.

Concentrations of oil were highest and degradation slowest in the intertidal and subtidal zones of the Wild Harbor River-Wild Harbor complex; concentrations were lowest at stations farthest out in Buzzards Bay. For years after the spill, oil spread seaward from the areas of highest concentration. Fresh infusions of less-degraded oil from the 1969 spill leaked from the marsh or eroded from the shore and caused secondary kills at some sampling sites months and years after the spill. Even today, more than a decade later, fuel oil that is only somewhat degraded is still detectable in the peat and sediments of the river.

Changes in marine life matched in intensity and duration the gradient of oil concentrations [45]. Normally, seasonal changes in the composition of communities of benthic animals are small. Samples taken in the same season, such as summer, are most alike. After the 1969 spill, fluctuations in composition of the benthos at the heavily oiled stations were pronounced, and consisted of large sequential or successional changes over a period of years, instead of small seasonal changes. At minimally oiled stations and at the control station in Sippewissett Marsh, faunal changes were small and seasonal throughout the period of study.

After the initial kill, the first species to appear at the most severely oiled stations was the opportunistic polychaete worm *Capitella capitata*. This species indicates severe pollution (or severe natural stress). It can live and reproduce under conditions lethal to most other species. In the fall, winter, and spring of 1969-70, an essentially single-species culture of *Capitella* occupied the bottom at densities ranging from 75,000 to more than 225,000 worms per square meter. As concentrations of oil gradually lessened, densities of *Capitella* declined sharply, and slightly less opportunistic species occupied the bottom sediments. The decrease in the numbers of *Capitella* was also a response to this influx of new competitors and predators. Thereafter faunal change at these stations was continuous and rapid for at least three years.

At intermediately oiled stations, benthic life suffered reduction immediately after the spill, but not annihilation. After the first year, changes in composition of the benthos began to alter in character from successional to seasonal. By the end of the second year recovery had begun but was not very far advanced. The sediments differed from station to station, and under normal conditions the communities of animals were likewise dissimilar. When faunas at these stations were undergoing successional changes in the aftermath of the oil spill, however, samples taken at various stations on the same date were remarkably similar. Only in the last stages of succession, three years after the spill, did the faunas begin to reflect differences in sediments.

In contrast to faunas at severely and intermediately oiled stations, the biota at stations that were either unaffected or only slightly oiled by the 1969 *Florida* spill exhibited small, normal recurring seasonal shifts in population throughout the sampling period.

The fact that the benthic fauna has returned to the pre-spill composition does not mean that damage has ceased. For example, Krebs and Burns [23] showed that juvenile fiddler crabs in moderately oiled sediments dug burrows too shallow to protect them from freezing in winter. Adult fiddler crabs suffered oil-induced effects on the locomotor and behavioral responses. Seven years after the spill, these combined effects continued to reduce greatly the fiddler crab populations in Wild Harbor marsh. Even today, more than a decade later, residues of the fuel oil spilled into Buzzards Bay by the barge *Florida* are still present in the marsh sediments of the Wild Harbor River Estuary. A single influx of oil from a rather small spill has caused chronic pollution that still persists.

Only through similar detailed, exacting, long-term studies can society appreciate the true price paid for the undramatic, pervasive, and ever-spreading chronic pollution that disrupts and alters increasingly greater reaches of natural habitats. Such rigorous investigations are woefully few. Yet it is precisely this sort of study that provides the only justifiable basis for valid, meaningful decisions.

The Mackin Report

In the arena of basic research, scientific papers must pass critical peer review and must appear in reputable journals. Too much of the scientific information in the area of applied science, however, has not passed these two fundamental safeguards. Such self-serving 'grey' literature has been widely distributed and effectively used by vested interests to influence policy. An example of such abuse is the uncritical acceptance of the Mackin Report.

With the Exxon Company as his publisher and distributor, Dr. A. G. Mackin of Texas A & M University reviewed our early unpublished Progress Reports of the *Florida* spill as well as a few other investigations [27]. In unusually strong language, Mackin severely criticizes our work, which is, he says, ". . . probably the least competent of all analyses of oil spills." His own conclusion is that "oil poses little serious threat to marine life."

At that time Congress was considering legislation for offshore oil development. Mackin's widely-distributed critique inundated legislative chambers. Owing to the potential impact of this piece of 'grey' literature, the *New Engineer* magazine decided Mackin's paper required an impartial review. "We tried for a year and could not find a single scientist willing to take on the task," the editor says. "A reviewer who criticized Mackin might have difficulty securing research money from the two largest sources — oil companies and the federal government."

Exactly this sort of thing makes us fear for the integrity of science in the face of considerable economic and political power. If our work were to be viewed free of Mackin's distortion we had to set the record straight. We felt compelled to provide a thorough critique of the Mackin report; this critique appeared in *New Engineer* in May, 1974 [44].

Mackin claims that the initial mass mortality was due to wind and waves, not to oil. Wind and waves could not possibly have been the responsible agents. The kill, visible to all, was on the shores of Wild Harbor River and adjacent flats, protected by surrounding land. The Wild Harbor River has only enough fetch to generate waves a few inches high. On two of the five days when dead and dying invertebrates and fish were washing ashore, the maximal wind velocities were 30 knots. There were 62 days in 1969 when the maximal wind velocities exceeded 30 knots, ten days when wind velocities reached 50 knots or greater; the greatest velocity measured in that year was 80 knots. Only immediately after the oil spill were any concentrations of dead invertebrates and fish observed. Mackin's indictment of wind and wave is absolutely untenable.

Mackin would have us believe that the exponential increase in the worm *Capitella* was a normal seasonal response to lowered temperatures. After the spill, the worm reached concentrations of 75,000 to more than 225,000 individuals per square meter for six months before declining. We attributed this very high density to the annihilation of most of the original fauna by the oil spill, giving the hardy opportunist a chance to fill the vacuum. The average number was 74 times larger than that in the same season a year later; there was not an explosive increase of *Capitella* in the nearby, uncontaminated Sippewissett Marsh. The experiments of Grassle and Grassle [17] demonstrate that *Capitella* does not bloom in response to low temperatures; Reish [30] showed it to be an indicator of more heavily oiled sediments in Long Beach harbor, California. Mackin's proposal is unsupported.

Mackin makes false assumptions about sediment composition and salinity gradients, and uses them to suggest that there was no offshore kill. He invokes erroneous interpretations of our data to 'prove' absence of a subtidal kill. Mackin employs muddled numbers and a poorly chosen index to arrive at a conclusion that is wrong, even by his own calculations.

He handles the chemical aspect of the West Falmouth study with perhaps even less competence than he does the biology. He says that our study of the persistence and fate of the oil "presents nothing new and is not worth taking time to discuss." In an interdepartmental memo the late and highly respected Dr. Max Blumer stated: "Our investigation at West Falmouth was the first and remains the only long-term study to use this objective technique [gas chromatography, now in nearly universal use] in assessing the persistence and fate of spilled oil. By denying the significance of these data, Dr. Mackin denies himself the insight into the environmental fate of fossil fuels."

The Gulf Universities Research Consortium/Offshore Ecology Investigation

How valid are studies that have appeared in the 'grey' literature and that have been used extensively in policy-making? By far the most widely publicized and frequently quoted is the Offshore

Ecology Investigation (OEI) by the Gulf Universities Research Consortium (GURC), conducted in Timbalier Bay and on the adjacent shelf of central Louisiana. Since about 1947 this area has been the site of the largest and most active oil production operations in the marine environment. The investigation, the keystone of research supported by the oil industry, was carried out over two years by 23 principal investigators from 14 universities and research institutes, and cost the 80 participating oil and oil-related companies more than $1.5 million [18]. The stated objective was the determination of the extent to which petroleum exploration, drilling, and production have significant irreversible effects on the ecological health of this stretch of Louisiana coast. API spokesman and senior lobbyist Edward Mertens [31] says OEI is "undoubtedly the most comprehensive study concerning the effects of chronic exposure to marine life ever attempted."

Thousands of pages of data collected by the investigators were submitted to four men who wrote the Consensus Report [34]. This document has been widely distributed. The frequently quoted report emphasizes the apparent good health of Gulf waters and concludes that ". . . low-level chronic exposure to crude oil has, at most, negligible effect on marine life." Mertens considers that the studies prove "Timbalier Bay has not undergone significant ecological change. Every indication of good ecological health is present."

How faithfully does this Consensus Report reflect the contents of the individual reports submitted by the principal investigators? Were some kinds of information omitted? Were the conclusions valid? Can the same data be construed another, more cogent way? Were some fundamental aspects of the investigation omitted from the GURC/OEI Program?

Because the findings of long-term chronic effects from the *Florida* spill [45] differed very much from the conclusions of the GURC/OEI Investigation as reported in the Final Project Planning Consensus Report [34], we obtained and critiqued most of the Final Reports, the primary source of data for the GURC Offshore Ecology Investigation. Our conclusions from this review follow.

The Consensus Report does not mention the doubts and misgivings voiced by a number of principal investigators [6, 13, 24,

33, 36] about the validity of the control sites in the GURC/OEI study area, both in Timbalier Bay and on the nearby Louisiana Shelf. Neither the reports of principal investigators nor the Consensus Report show locations of production and drilling platforms on the Louisiana and nearby Texas Shelf or in Timbalier Bay. Without such information it is impossible to judge the validity of the selected controls.

For reasons of navigational safety, the positions of offshore platforms appear on U.S.C.G.S. navigational charts. We counted 2,600 platforms that were continuously present along the Louisiana and Texas coasts. This number is a minimum. In the GURC study, two platforms and their controls, one in Timbalier Bay and the other on the adjacent Louisiana Shelf, were the sites of intensive study. Current velocities [35] reveal the short time in which water moves from the offshore production platform to its control site nine kilometers away. Our calculations from Oetking's data show that contaminants carried in the water can reach the offshore control site from platforms as far away as Southwest Pass within a very few days for at least half the year. Extrapolating the frequent incidences of low-level pollution documented at both the offshore and the Timbalier Bay production platforms selected for study, to the thousands of other active platforms shows that the entire inner shelf of Louisiana and part of the adjoining Texas Shelf are uniformly contaminated with petroleum hydrocarbons. The lack of differences between the production platform and its control is not, therefore, evidence for a lack of adverse effects from oil extraction operations, as maintained by some of the individual studies and by the Consensus Report. This lack indicates, instead, uniform pollution of the entire inshore shelf of Louisiana by oil industry activities.

GURC/OEI claims that bacteria degrade hydrocarbons as rapidly as they are discharged through the oil industry activities on the Louisiana shelf [36]. It proposes a model, based on laboratory studies, in which bacterial degradation keeps the concentration of petroleum hydrocarbons in dynamic equilibrium on the entire inner Louisiana Shelf. This model is unrealistic: the very high concentrations of nutrients used in the laboratory to produce this rate of degradation are impossibly greater than those actually attained in nature. Even under these idealized laboratory conditions of elevated temperatures and well-oxygenated, nutrient-enriched sea-water, the aromatic hydrocarbons are hardly altered. The Consensus Report does not mention these limitations and barely refers to the model itself.

Spilled oil quickly passes from the water column to the sea floor and into bottom sediments. Some of the more readily available papers documenting this phenomenon are Blumer and Sass [3], Cabioch et al. [8], Johnsson [21], Conover [9], Kolpack [22], Scarratt and Zitko [46], and Spooner [47]. This settling and incorporation are entirely excluded from GURC/OEI, a critical omission. Failure of the Consensus Report to consider bottom sediments as a sink for spilled oil seriously compromises the Report's credibility. Total concentrations of hydrocarbons in the sediments are very high [25], at levels shown to be stressful or lethal in the West Falmouth study [45]. GURC investigators did not distinguish petroleum-derived hydrocarbons from naturally occurring ones. Since the prime objective was to evaluate the impact oil industry activities had on the marine biota, the failure of GURC/OEI to attempt this crucial separation is inexplicable.

Because primary productivity, or the rate at which organic matter is produced by phytoplankton in the GURC/OEI study area is among the highest in the Gulf of Mexico [13], and because water depths there are shallow, one should expect large populations of benthic animals in relatively unstressed conditions. Compared to densities found in other benthic areas in Europe and North America [44, 32, 28, 29, 30, 12, 38, 42, 43, 4, 26, 11], densities in the GURC/OEI area were very low [24, 14, 15, 53, 16]. Despite the allegation that species present in the GURC/OEI area indicate a 'healthy' benthic environment, most of the bottom-living animals there belong to two highly opportunistic species shown in other studies to indicate highly stressed environments [4, 40, 5, 20, 9, 41, 49, 50, 51, 52].

Farrell, the one investigator of the benthos who did not qualify his conclusions and did not question the sampling program or the controls [14, 15], was the one who stated unequivocally that activities of the oil industry had not been detrimental to the benthic fauna. His version is that which most closely approximates the interpretation in the Consensus Report and which is the basis for the claims of 'good ecological health' made by the oil industry. He had, however, manipulated his data in a variety of unacceptable ways that falsely produced exaggeratedly higher diversity values and thus 'greater ecological health.' Even more disturbing are the very great differences in densities reported in his and in another GURC study by Kritzler [24] for the same animal group sampled at the same times and at the same stations.

The Offshore Ecology Investigation, 1979

In the summer of 1980, a 589-page paper dealing exclusively with the Offshore Ecology Investigations appeared [54]. More than four-fifths of this publication deals with the Principal Investigators' Reports, and about one-seventh with a reappraisal by Bender, Reish, and Ward, of the earlier Offshore Ecology Investigation. We have not had time to review carefully and critically these 1979 versions of the GURC/OEI Principal Investigators' Final Reports or to attempt a detailed critique of the re-examination by Bender et al. of the Offshore Ecology Investigation. Superficial examination shows that several of these later versions of the Principal Investigators' Reports differ from the original reports written in 1974, on which the Consensus Report is purportedly based. Because interpretations presented in the Final Consensus Report were aggressively and effectively used to influence policy, it is proper that differences between the 1974 and later version of the same Principal Investigators' Report be clearly expressed and explained. So far as we can discern, no such correction or explanation is offered.

Particularly obvious in our cursory perusal is the absence in the 1979 version of any of the hydrocarbon data presented in the 1974 Final Report by Laseter and Ledet. Theirs is that essential report upon which most of the other studies rest. Their work is especially vital because it provides the only data on hydrocarbon concentrations in the bottom sediments, a major sink for petroleum discharged into the overlying water.

In the independent appraisal of the Offshore Ecology Investigation, Bender et al. concur with our conclusions that the control sites were invalid. They also cite the doubts about the adequacies of the controls voiced by the Principal Investigators, including many workers noted previously in our paper, but never aired in the Consensus Report [34]. Bender et al. believe ". . . the OEI Council Conclusions (Morgan et al., 1974) should be reviewed and restated to indicate clearly the limitations of the experimental design and the data base for definitely answering questions on chronic effects of oil." Bender and his colleagues do not address the appropriateness of the conclusion in the Consensus Report that bacteria degrade chronically discharged oil at a rate that keeps concentrations of petroleum hydrocarbons on the Louisiana Shelf in equilibrium. They also do not discuss the questionable model upon which this conclusion is based. Again, they do not comment on the total omission from the OEI of the critical transfer of spilled oil from the water column onto the bottom, except obliquely, by stating the need to use ". . . the most advanced analytical support for quantifying hydrocarbons in the most likely sinks, especially in sediments and organisms." They do observe that "there were insufficient sediment samples analyzed for hydrocarbons in the OEI to assess adequately buildup or possible effects on benthic organisms."

Despite various caveats, Bender et al. concur with the major conclusion in the Consensus Report that every indication of good ecological health is present. They base their agreement on the fact that the study area has one of the highest rates of primary productivity and secondary productivity (the rate at which organic matter is produced by herbivorous zooplankton) in the Gulf of Mexico and that it is extremely organic-rich. They also think that ". . . if there had been a buildup of hydrocarbons and other pollutants, then one would expect a reduced benthic fauna and the appearance of pollution-tolerant species, such as *Capitella capitata*, in large numbers at the affected localities," a condition they believe is not indicated by the OEI benthic studies. Our own analysis refutes their interpretation by showing that, despite the fact that the ecosystem is rich in nutrients, the density of benthic fauna is, indeed, decidedly lower than densities in other areas, and that the majority of the benthos in the OEI study area is composed of two species, both known to be precise indicators of severely polluted environments.

In their appraisal, Bender et al. do not question the improper manipulation of data in one of the benthic studies ([14, 15] that falsely creates exaggeratedly high diversities, that, in turn, support the contention of 'good ecological health.' They uncritically accept and use questionable data in their appraisal, such as certain nutrient concentrations [7], orders of magnitude higher than those any chemist would expect to find, or falsely high concentrations of silica [7] from samples stored in glass jars that are themselves composed of silica.

We must emphasize that our remarks about the Independent Appraisal of the Offshore Ecology Investigation by Bender, Reish, and Ward are observations made from a brief perusal of their paper. Their efforts deserve a careful, detailed, thoughtful critique by the scientific community.

Why did GURC feel the need to re-evaluate its earlier Consensus Report? Were the stimulus questions about its inherent validity? We noted in our preliminary findings of the GURC Offshore Ecology Investigation that valid control stations did not exist, and that a number of Principal Investigators expressed in the Final Reports the same doubts, none of which appeared in the Consensus Report. In order to warn interested public officials and scientific colleagues that conclusions in the Consensus Report are of doubtful value, we presented our findings in public lectures. It is perhaps fortuitous that our initial unpublished findings and the conclusions reached by Bender et al. in their reappraisal should agree. In contrast, some of our findings made later in our critique of the GURC/OEI and not widely communicated disagreed sharply with those of Bender et al. For example, we found compelling evidence for severe impact of oil industry activities on the benthic fauna, whereas Bender and his colleagues concur with the Consensus Report that the benthic studies revealed every indication of good ecological health.

The Ekofisk Oilfield Study

What validity has a fate-and-effects study of possible oil pollution resulting from oil extraction off the Louisiana coast when this study was carried out 34 and 35 years after operations began?

If marked changes had occurred, they almost certainly would have begun in the early stages of oil exploitation and become obvious within the next few years. As with the GURC Offshore Investigation, the few attempts to measure such effects were nearly always carried out many years after this critical early period of operation.

Fortunately, the investigation of the Ekofisk oilfield by Addy, Levell, and Hartley [1] does provide information on effects that can occur during the first few years of oil industry activities. The first survey was made in August 1973, almost concurrently with the start of extraction operations [12], the second in August 1975, the third in August 1977 [1]. The twenty-four stations were arranged in a series of transects radiating from a complex of a storage tank and two nearly production platforms. The total area covered was approximately 126 square kilometers, with the most remote stations approximately six kilometers from the central complex. Faunal, hydrocarbon, and sediment samples were taken at each sampling site.

The first survey revealed that there were no significant differences in community structure among the stations. The sediments, fine sands, were remarkably homogeneous in the study area, and water depths varied only between 67 and 71 meters [12]. By 1975, total densities were somewhat reduced close to the storage tank and production facility. By 1977, the area of low faunal densities had spread, and at the innermost stations numbers of species, total densities, and densities of many individual species were much lower than those at stations more remote from the center. At the same time, concentrations of hydrocarbons in sediments close to the storage and production facility were much greater than those in sediments at more distant stations. Concentrations of extractable organic compounds were high near the storage tank and one of the production platforms; concentrations of aromatic hydrocarbons, derived mainly from petroleum, were much higher at the innermost stations. The unresolved envelope of gas chromatographs, representing the amount of undegraded hydrocarbons, were again the highest in the analyses of samples from stations closest to the installations. Finally, the ratios between the straight-chain paraffin molecules n-C_{18} to n-C_{29}, which measure relative quantities of undegraded crude oil and naturally occurring hydrocarbons, were highest around one of the production platforms. These data clearly demonstrate the effects of chronic low-level pollution resulting from oil industry activities on the benthic fauna in the critical early period of operation in a new oil field.

Addy and his colleagues seem to have carried out a solid and valid investigation showing chronic adverse effects of oil production that became evident during the first few years of operation. We should be cautious, though, in making generalizations from this one important study, for our knowledge is still limited. Hartley (in press), who participated in the Ekofisk oilfield research program, undertook a similar investigation in the Forties oilfield in the North Sea using procedures and analyses comparable to those employed in the Ekofisk surveys. He made two surveys, one prior to development, the other three years later, in June, 1978. He found little change in densities and faunal composition. Sediments and water depth were much more variable in the Forties than in the Ekofisk area; faunal differences that were found could be related to differences in sediment composition, in water depth, or in both. Concentrations of hydrocarbons in the sediments were low throughout the Forties oilfield study area.

The Coal Oil Point Study

Another study cited by Mertens [31] purporting to show that "Low-level chronic exposure of crude oil has, at most, negligible effect on marine life" is the investigation by Dr. Dale Straughan of benthic fauna exposed to natural seepage of oil at Coal Oil Point, near Santa Barbara, California. She compared the fauna at Coal Oil Point to that at control sites at which natural seepage does not occur and oil residues in the sediments are minor or absent. Her final report [48], submitted to the American Petroleum Institute's Environmental Affairs Department, is claimed by API to be the "most definitive, careful, detailed, scientifically documented investigation ever undertaken."

Every day fifty to 100 barrels of oil seep into the water at Coal Oil Point. Does the fauna in the chronically oiled sediments differ from that in the unoiled control sites? Actual densities of specimens and species are not given in Straughan's report. Instead, the numbers of individuals of a species in the various samples were 'standardized' prior to analysis. For instance, if the highest density of species A in any sample was 100, then occurrence of this species in three other samples at densities of 20, 10 and 2 would be shown as 20%, 10%, and 2%, respectively. If, on the other hand, the highest density for species B was 2, then 1 individual in a sample would be recorded as 50%.

By reversing the standardization procedure, we found that among the 68 polychaete species included in the study, almost 40% had standardized densities of 100 and 0, or one individual at most in a sample. At this minimal possible density of one, presence or absence in a sample is mere random chance. It is to be expected that comparison of faunas from Coal Oil Point and from control sites produces a random pattern. Thus, that result of the Coal Oil Point investigation cited as very significant, the supposed fact that "There was no relationship between abundance or presence/absence of any group of organisms and petroleum hydrocarbons in sediments," reflects instead the apparently extremely low densities of many of the species included in the analysis, densities so low that they must inevitably yield a random pattern. Straughan's study tells us nothing about deleterious effects of chronic oil pollution.

We were frustrated in our attempt to interpret the standardized densities for most of the remaining species. For example, one species was collected in 17 of the 82 samples; 12 times at standardized densities of 45%, 2 times at 63%, 2 times at 77% and one time at 100%. This series of numbers does not factor. We found similar problems with most of the other species having densities greater than one in a sample.
the other species having densities greater than one in a sample.

On December 20, 1977, one of us wrote Dr. Straughan of our concerns, and asked her to send us the raw data — that is, the actual faunal composition of each sample and the actual number of individuals of each species. We asked Dr. Straughan whether we had unwittingly misconstrued her methodology and, if so, that she correct us. She responded in a letter dated January 19, 1978, as follows:

You cannot deduce actual numbers of specimens from the dendro-grams. The data show relative abundance for a particular species in each sample. The way it is presented also does not provide 'between species abundance comparisons.'

We are currently reworking these samples and trying to complete identification of all groups. When this is complete, we should be in a position to provide raw data.

A second letter sent to Dr. Straughan on January 31, 1978, pointed out that our request was for only that raw data forming the basis for her published final report, *Sublethal Effects of Natural Chronic Exposure to Petroleum in the Marine Environment*. There was no response to this registered letter or to a third registered letter sent on August 14, 1978.

More than three years have elapsed since we requested the raw data. The Coal Oil Point Study by Dale Straughan, like the GURC Offshore Ecology Investigation, has been a strong influence on decision-making and policy. Yet, the unanswered questions once again raise the urgent question of how legislators, the public, and the scientific community itself can properly evaluate technical literature when the information on which such studies are based is not available or is very difficult to obtain.

Epilogue

This journey of discovery suggests that the essential feature of representative government, checks and balances, seems not to exist in that area of participatory democracy just explored. The oil in-dustry supports much of the research on oil pollution; oil-industry lobbyists make the preponderance of the contacts with decision-makers regarding oil pollution. The information and scientific data that will form the basis of environmental policy are not ex-posed to the adversary system, at least not openly. To guard its integrity the community engaged in basic research demands that a work of science, to be accepted, must pass peer review and must appear in a reputable scientific journal. Does not the integrity of the decision-making process equally demand that such procedures be applied uniformly and without exception to the more immedi-ately relevant aspects of applied research, such as pollution biology, in which the potentials and incentives for abuse are so great? Peer review is not infallible. In applied research, however, this review would tend to ensure that the scientific literature upon which public policy is based is openly evaluated and easily available. Peer review ought to be part of the dialogue between the scientific community and the government.

Governmental regulatory agencies whose mission includes environmental protection were instituted as counterweights to powerful interests, such as the oil industry, which have almost limitless resources to influence public opinion, public officials, and public policy. Unfortunately, in the case of environmental protection, it has been a dismal mismatch.

The regulatory agencies suffer from a number of weaknesses that seriously compromise their effectiveness in protecting the environment. They are large and unwieldy and are therefore unable to respond effectively or efficiently to their mandate. They suffer from the Trojan Horse Syndrome whereby officials or other personnel on temporary leave from the very industries being regulated fill sensitive middle and high posts in the regulatory agency, where they are in admirable positions to continue working on behalf of their own companies. Selection by the Reagan Administration of directors who are philosophically or actively opposed to the mission of their own agencies gives the Trojan Horse Syndrome full scope.

In the regulatory agencies, and in government bureaucracy generally, leadership, initiative, and courage to speak out on issues are often not conducive to extended careers. Survival and promotion are too often the rewards of keeping a low profile and not making waves. Such a system of rewards devastates those idealists who joined an agency to pursue meaningful and socially positive careers according to its mandatae. Not surprisingly, morale is usually low and esprit de corps slight in these agencies. Initiative and creative thought wither, positive action sinks into the bureaucratic morass. For all these reasons, inordinate amounts of time, effort, and human resources secure only slight progress.

How, then, do we redress and ensure the true checks and balances that ought to exist between the oil industry and the regulatory agencies, especially since these agencies may well suffer

further emasculation by the present administration? Are the regu-
to effectively protect the environment? Perhaps the most effective
effectively to protect the environment? Perhaps the most effective
advocates today are in the private sector, those millions of Americans deeply concerned about our environment. The problem,
then, is the active expression of the great political strength of this
constituency and the translation of its concerns into public policy.

The most obvious agents for restoring the balance are the
conservation organizations and foundations. They should not
compete, as they do now, in many voices and with only slightly
differing nuances, for the attention and support of the same constituencies. They should unite to speak with a single clear voice.
They should make ringingly clear to their constituencies and to
the nation their deep concern for the present deteriorating political climate for environmental advocacy, the probably reduced
role such advocacy will play in decisions about public policy, and
the urgent sense that this potentially disastrous trend must be
halted and reversed.

To this end the environmental alliance should institute a leading
agency to represent it, just as the American Petroleum Institute
represents the entire petroleum industry. Such an agency could be
a clearing house for environmental matters for the constituent
conservation groups; a resource center on environmental matters
for conservation groups, educators, elected representatives, governmental agencies, the legal profession, the business community,
and the general public; and the core for political action. It could
unite the considerable potential strength of the total environmental
movement and then exert that strength to greatest effect at the
critical times and places within the political system.

From our first-hand experience, we suggest that another important and proper part of the mandate of the leading agency is the
careful examination of the quality and validity of the scientific
evidence used to make policy about the environment. This most
important critical function, the necessity of which has hardly been
expressed elsewhere, is the major theme of this essay. This obligation should and properly does belong within the purview of the
Federal Government as representative of all the people. The responsible agencies obviously lack the stomach, the will, and,

perhaps, the freedom to fulfill their charge. To exercise its function of review within its mandate, this leading agency for the environmental consortium must assemble a team of competent, dedicated, strongly motivated, responsible experts, primarily natural scientists, as well as some social and political scientists, engineers, lawyers, and economists. The obvious and very great contribution of this group is the assurance that the major scientific information upon which policy is to be based is closely scrutinized for validity of methods and interpretation, and that the findings and conclusions are made readily available to all interested parties. Another wholesome product of such critical and open reviews will be to prevent the use of both biased proprietory research in which findings favorable to the interests of the sponsors are released while deleterious findings are buried, and to prevent the use of that rampant, often insidious, self-serving 'grey' literature discussed earlier in this essay. The ultimate result should be public policy that is less likely to be based on faulty information, misrepresentation, and poor science.

Another worthy endeavor that the consortium might undertake is the support of research in the environmental realm. Intellectual climate profoundly affects the quality of science. This relationship is little understood or appreciated except by working scientists and those immediately interacting with them.

Probably in response to the immediate needs of those in government for scientific data to formulate environmental laws and policy, funding agencies have chosen to support short-term research programs, for the most part. Owing to the insufficiency of time allowed, the resulting studies are often at best superficial and equivocal.

A problem perhaps even more severe is the insidious, pervasive and stultifying effects of bureaucracy itself. In large, bold type is a fundamental and inviolate truth: the larger the bureaucracy, the smaller the creative scientific achievement. It is tragic that most people trained in applied environmental science, particularly those in government or those whose research is funded by government or industry, work in a highly structured, dehumanized, bureaucratic climate. All those factors conducive and essential to scientific endeavor — motivation, creativity, enthusiasm, dedication to excellence, personal involvement, professional pride, leadership, high morale, the time to think through a problem, and the resulting satisfaction and fulfillment of meaningful achievement — inevitably wither. What should be a satisfying and purposeful life-work degenerates into a stressed and barely tolerable 9-to-5 existence. The results are the massive waste of needed talent and the squandering of economic resources available for environmental studies.

The environmental consortium can best resolve this dilemma by supporting a small number of complementary, long-term environmental studies, the results of which would be generally applicable. The consortium should invite the participation of the very best scientists and support staff, and should foster a climate as conducive as possible to good science. Studies so produced should then be models for a new generation of significantly more useful and more effective environmental research.

Can Marine Mammals Survive Man?

DOUGLAS G. CHAPMAN

DOUGLAS G. CHAPMAN
has directed the Center for Quantitative Science at the University
of Washington since 1969. From 1971-1980 he was also Dean
of the College of Fisheries. He has held a Guggenheim Fellowship
at Oxford University, and visiting positions at North Carolina
State University, at Scripps Institution of Oceanography, and
at the Southwest Fisheries Research Center in La Jolla, California.
He has chaired the Scientific Committee of the International
Whaling Commission and the Scientific Advisory Committee of the
Marine Mammal Commission, and is currently Chairman of the
Marine Mammal Commission. He has also advised the U.S.
delegations to several international fisheries commissions. His
research has focused on population enumeration and population
dynamics of fish and marine mammal populations.

Human threats to marine mammals such as seals, sea lions, manatees, sea otters, grey whales and others, are an old story, and ecology groups have had a good deal of success in rallying public opinion to stop the slaughter of these animals. Dr. Douglas Chapman, Director of the Center for Quantitative Science at the University of Washington and chairman of the U.S. Marine Mammals Commission, sketches in this essay a more subtle peril. Human use, or abuse, of the coastal habitat now represents the single most serious threat to the survival of many marine mammals.

Dr. Chapman says that it is no longer enough to "save the whale" or to "stop the seal slaughter." We must also preserve the habitat in which these mammals live and reproduce.

Tracing the laws and treaties which have prevented the extermination of some of these animals, Dr. Chapman finds the fabric of legislative measures designed to protect marine mammals to be a very weak safety net. He identifies gaping holes between the areas of coverage of three principal legal measures on which marine mammals depend for protection: the Marine Mammal Protection Act, the Coastal Zone Management Act of 1972, and the Endangered Species Act.

The threat is no longer one of direct human exploitation. Dr. Chapman outlines how human competition jeopardizes the habitat essential to the survival of the various marine mammals of our coasts.

THE PLIGHT of mammals — whales, dolphins, seals and sea otters — facing extinction elicits strong popular emotions. In the past, ecology groups have focused public concern on saving endangered species from exploitation at the hands of hunters. The task has been enormous, since for most of human history, marine mammals have been regarded either as objects to be utilized or pests to be eliminated.

Now, another, equally important requirement for protection of these animals emerges. It is human use of the coastal zone that now represents the most serious threat to marine mammals. Our coasts and nearshore islands play a vital role in their lives. Often unnoticed, it is a role which may hold the key to new strategies for protecting endangered species.

Ranging from direct competition for shoreline space to the less obvious effects of chronic pollution, human activity along the coast has a significant impact on these animals. Throughout the '80s, our task is to broaden general public concern for marine mammals into specific support for preserving critically important coastal habitats.

To accomplish this work, we will have to make difficult choices. Should public access to some beaches for recreational purposes be restricted to allow seals and sea lions an area for hauling out of the water and breeding? Should West Coast fishermen or sea otters be allowed to harvest commercially valuable shellfish? Should fishermen be required to provide special protection for dolphins or porpoises caught in nets?

A second sphere of coastal confrontation centers on the effect of pollution on these endangered species. Development — whether of cities or offshore oil fields — entails an inherent decrease in the cleanliness of surrounding waters. Chronic exposure to even low levels of some compounds can have serious effects on the marine environment. Contamination of a sea otter's coat with even small amounts of oil can render useless the animal's unique adaptation for survival in cold waters. Small shifts in the marine environment triggered by discharges from offshore petroleum production could disrupt the delicate food chain which supports the largest of all mammals, the whale.

International conservation measures, and especially the provisions of the U.S. Marine Mammal Protection Act of 1972, deal with overt actions affecting these animals. Nothing is said about actions, overt or otherwise, which affect marine mammal habitat. But both the Endangered Species Act and Coastal Zone Management Act do provide a framework for protecting coastal habitats.

While the Endangered Species Act permits the designation of critical habitats for any species listed as endangered, and may restrict activities in such critical habitats, little has been done to date along such lines. Part of the problem is that it is difficult for biologists to define what is the critical habitat for many marine mammals. It is therefore difficult to defend the setting aside of this critical habitat for marine mammals and to protect it from competing use.

Many coastal states have plans for development and control of shoreline areas under the Coastal Zone Management Act. Despite the critical role these areas play in the lives of many marine mammals, and despite the widespread concern for these species, state coastal management plans have been rather negligent in addressing these concerns. Integrating marine mammal protection into coastal zone management is a major challenge to the conservation movement and one which runs against a heritage of exploitation which first began along the shore.

A History of Exploitation

Long before they learned to build ocean-going vessels, humans had begun to hunt accessible groups of marine animals. Those that were able to survive did so either offshore, on remote islands, or in polar regions. Once western man became more adept at ocean travel, even those remote spots no longer served as sanctuaries. The decimation of marine mammals began. The record of exploitation from the later 1700's onward is indeed a sorry one. Ice breeding harp and hooded seals of the North Atlantic were reduced from several million to less than half their initial number in a few generations.

Between 1820 and 1860, hunters exterminated fur seal breeding populations on many islands of the southern ocean and on some of the Kurile Islands off Siberia. Before the slaughter was finally halted, the northern fur seals on the Pribilof Islands were reduced from a level of 2.5 million to less than one-fifth of that number. The Guadalupe fur seal was thought to be extinct for several decades of this century until Carl Hubbs joyfully reported a renewed sighting in 1954. On Guadalupe Island in the North Pacific a remnant population of elephant seal also escaped extermination. Elsewhere, walruses and sea lions were substantially reduced in numbers, but not to the same extent as fur seals.

Monk seals live in much warmer waters than most other seals — the Mediterranean, the Caribbean and the Leeward Islands of the Hawaiian chain. Their numbers have been severely depleted, though how many were killed for commercial purposes and how many were killed by fishermen as competitors is not known.

Two other groups of marine mammals were exploited even more severely than the fur seals: the sea otters of the North Pacific and the sirenians. The latter family includes manatees and dugongs as well as sea cows, which became extinct within a generation after Bering discovered them in 1741.

At one time sea otter populations ranged from Baja California northward along the Pacific coast of North America through the Aleutian and Pribilof chains to the coast of Siberia. Hunted relentlessly for its valuable fur, the sea otter began to disappear first from one part of its range, then another. In 1911, the United States, Russia, Japan and Great Britain (on behalf of Canada) signed a treaty protecting sea otters. The move came so late that the signers were not at all sure that any sea otters survived anywhere. Fortunately, there were remnant populations in the Aleutian Islands and in one isolated area off the coast of California south of Monterey.

Basque hunters were apparently the first to exploit whales in substantial numbers as early as the 13th century. Not until the 19th century, with advances in shipbuilding, however, did people begin to deplete whale populations. The easily hunted right and bowhead whales were severely reduced, followed early in the 20th century by the gray and humpback whales, both residents of near coastal waters. Even the deep ocean dwellers — blue, fin and sei whales — have not been immune, since World War II, from pelagic or open sea whaling expeditions.

Exploitation of the smaller cetaceans, such as dolphins and porpoises, has been much more sporadic and localized since it has been carried out largely by primitive methods for local consumption. One exception is the bottlenose whale hunted in the 50's and 60's by Norwegian commercial vessels in the North Atlantic.

Ironically, the largest kill of dolphins and porpoises occurs by accident, the unintentional and tragic sidenote to the methodical hunt for tuna in the central eastern tropical Pacific Ocean. In one year during the 1960s, an estimated half million dolphins and porpoises died as a result of tuna fishing.

Human exploitation of the various mammals of the sea had become a threat to the very survival of some species, and the source of enormous public outcry. In the 1960s and 1970s, the United

States, both alone and in concert with those other nations willing to cooperate began to forge new laws and treaties to protect the marine mammals.

Legal Protections for Marine Mammals

Slowly, in the 20th century, a degree of restraint has been brought to the exploitation of these animals. An international agreement forbade killing of fur seals in 1911. In the 1960s, the International Whaling Commission was pressured into giving protection to the most severely depleted species and reducing the quotas on other types of whales.

Other species, such as elephant seals, received *de facto* protection once populations were reduced to such levels it was no longer profitable to hunt them. In the meantime, public opposition intensified to bounty hunting, seal reduction programs, and the large porpoise kill in the yellow fin purse seine tuna fishery.

These objections to killing marine mammals found their clearest expression in the U.S. Marine Mammal Protection Act of 1972. The act protected sea otters, provided for elimination of open sea fur sealing, and led to more rational management of this industry. The act places a moratorium with some exceptions on the "taking" of marine mammals. Taking is rather broadly defined to include harassment, capture, killing or attempting any of these acts. However, some of the exceptions are pertinent. The harvest of fur seals on the Pribilof Islands, off Alaska, carried out under the North Pacific Fur Seal Treaty, is exempted as are kills by Alaska natives for subsistence. Fishermen with a permit may carry out operations which accidentally involve marine mammals and which may kill them, as long as the species in question is not "depleted."

The Marine Mammal Protection Act of the United States was the first legislation of such broad protective scope. Other countries have followed suit and passed legislation to protect their own animals and/or to restrict imports of marine mammal products in order to discourage their exploitation elsewhere. At the same time environmental and conservation groups have applied even more pressure to the International Whaling Commission. They have succeeded in changing its methods of management and increased the protection of whale species whose status is uncertain. This action has given protection to many more stocks of whales. Annual world catches of great whales — which once exceeded 60,000 — have now been reduced below 15,000.

While some exploitation of various species of northern fur seals, whales and porpoises still goes on for subsistence purposes in Alaska, it is mostly on a relatively small scale, and is generally under control.

It is worth noting that all of these legal protections, especially the "taking" of the Marine Mammal Protection Act, deal with overt human acts. They do not address the equally urgent issue of protecting the coastal environment in which these mammals exist. Heretofore concern for marine mammals has concentrated on giving them positive protection from exploitation. We must now address the more subtle task of preventing or eliminating threats to their coastal habitat.

Sea Otters

Sea otter populations, totally protected since 1911, have made an impressive comeback from earlier decimation, particularly in Alaska where the population is estimated to exceed 100,000. In California, the number is smaller since the surviving nucleus from which the stock rebuilt was much smaller. An estimated 1,800 sea otters range from just south of Pismo Beach to just north of Santa Cruz. Their density is about eleven per mile of coast in this area. In recent years they have become quite a tourist attraction, particularly in the Monterey area. A female otter and her offspring playing or feeding in the nearshore kelp beds presents such an idyllic scene that it is hard to realize they are the center of controversy. The sources of the controversy are twofold: human effect on the otters, and the otters' effect on abalone and shellfish that are harvested commercially or for sport.

Both problems relate to the otter's need to keep warm in rather cold water. Unlike whales and pinnipeds (seals and walruses) which have blubber to insulate against this cold environment, the sea otter maintains its body temperature through the insulation of air in its fur and by maintaining a high metabolic rate. Provided it is clean, sea otter fur serves as an excellent insulator. Thus a sea otter spends a substantial amount of time grooming itself. If the fur becomes soiled, its insulation value is substantially reduced, and the sea otter is likely to die. Consequently an oil spill could have a very serious impact on a sea otter population, particularly if the oil were to collect in the kelp beds that serve as refuges for the otters. The possibility of a widespread oil spill led, at least in part, to the recent designation by the U.S. Fish and Wildlife Service of the California sea otter as "threatened."

A very high metabolic rate is the otter's second defense against cold water. Because of this high metabolic rate, the sea otter eats a prodigious amount, perhaps as much as 25 per cent of its body weight daily. Even a relatively low density of sea otters — such as is found off the California coast — can have a large impact on the nearshore communities of shellfish, their primary food. Fishermen insist that a viable shellfish fishery and a sea otter population are incompatible.

Transplant Program

To reduce the potential damage from an oil spill or other local disaster to sea otters, it is clearly desirable that the otters' range be enlarged. This can be brought about through the natural expansion that has occurred for the past 70 years either through a gradual extension of both ends of the range, or through transplantation. Both forms of expansion meet resistance from those who wish to utilize shellfish — clams and abalones — for commercial or sport purposes. Of course, no legal action can be taken to stop natural expansion. There is some evidence, however, of illegal actions. Occasionally otters have been found dead from gunshot wounds.

Sea otter transplantation has been tried on a number of occasions. In the late 1960s and early 1970s otters were moved to Oregon, Washington, British Columbia (Vancouver Island), and southeastern Alaska. Of these, only the transplant to southeastern

Alaska can be declared successful. The move to Oregon has almost certainly failed, while the outcome of the Washington and British Columbia transplants remains in doubt.

Much has been learned through these transplants. Future efforts would carry a higher probability of success. Still, a number of questions remain unsolved. From where should the otters be moved — the ends or center of the range? What are the most ecologically desirable new locations? What are the politically acceptable transplant locations? What are the minimum numbers to transplant to achieve a reasonable probability of success? What transplantation losses are tolerable in otter management?

While those questions remain unanswered, there has been considerable research activity in the past several years on sea otter ecology and on the ecosystem they inhabit in Alaska and in California. Estes and others have demonstrated that in Alaska the inshore faunal and floral community is radically altered when sea otters move in; sea urchins are substantially reduced and the kelps on which sea urchins feed are able to flourish once more. In California the interaction between sea otters and other elements of the community are more complex. One puzzling aspect is the substantially lower density and population growth rate of otters in California as contrasted to their proliferation in several locales in Alaska. Both factors must be considered in the planning now underway for management of the California sea otter. Such planning is part of a recovery plan required under the Endangered Species Act. Such a recovery plan should lead to steps that will eventually make it possible to remove the otter from the list of threatened species.

To ensure long term viability of the California sea otter population, some transplantation apparently will have to be undertaken. There are some places to which sea otters can never return due to industrial and human activities on the shoreline. Other places may be denied them because of political opposition. Until the biological and political questions associated with transplantation are resolved, the sea otter's future is at best uncertain. It is a future tied to coastal development which may render more areas unsuitable for colonization. In this sense, a sea otter recovery plan must be integrated with coastal management.

Seals and Sea Lions

The United States has many different seals: the gray seal of New England; the harbor seal on both coasts and Alaska; the elephant seals off California; the monk seal on some of the outer Hawaiian islands; and several ice seals off Alaska. In addition, there is the California sea lion, so well known as a circus and aquarium performer; and its larger relative, the Stellar, or northern, sea lion, that lives from central California northward along the Pacific coast. All of these were hunted — for profit or as "varmints" — and seriously reduced or depleted. All except the fur seal are now protected, although some incidental kill by fishermen occurs and there is the subsistence hunting by Alaska natives. As a result of the protection, seal populations have been rebuilding at differing rates. Those species occupying relatively undisturbed offshore islands or living in Alaska are rebuilding rapidly, while seals are repopulating much more slowly in areas with more intense coastal development.

Fishermen in various areas strongly oppose protection of these animals. They assert that marine mammals damage both nets and catch and compete for fish. A typical situation occurs in the Columbia river estuary where harbor seals, probably from adjacent coastal areas, congregate during salmon runs.

Undoubtedly, some seals do take fish from fishermen's nets. Until recently, despite substantial anecdotal information, quantitative assessment of the damage done by marine mammals to catches or nets has been lacking. A study by Frank Fay and Craig Matkin of Alaska has provided such information for the Copper River delta of Alaska, and another study now underway should provide such data for the Columbia River Estuary. The Fay-Matkin study also provided estimates of marine mammals killed (in violation of the Marine Mammal Protection Act) by fishermen in this conflict.

A second impediment to increases of seals and sea lions is pollution and the effects of oil and/or heavy metals. Even though a few laboratory experiments have been completed and a number of observations made in the wild of animals beset by oil spills, the impact of this contamination is not clear. In a comprehensive summary on the effects of oil, Joseph Geraci and David St. Aubin suggest that, while healthy animals may not be seriously injured by oil pollution, they may be "more vulnerable to the effects of oil during moult, reproduction, times of low food availability or when weakened by parasites and diseases."

In the early 1970s, a high incidence of premature births and pup losses occurred on the harbor seal colony of Gertrude Island in Puget Sound, Washington. High levels of DDT and similar compounds were found in some of the dead animals, suggesting a cause and effect relationship. This inference is strengthened by the apparent disappearance of the problem after the 1972 banning of DDT.

Though not in any systematic manner, assays have been carried out for such compounds and heavy metals on a variety of pinnipeds. High levels of mercury have been found in fur seals and sea lions, but similar or even higher levels have also been found in Antarctic seals. Both the cause of the concentrations and the effects of such high levels on the well-being of the animals remain obscure.

Coastal Conflict

While fisheries conflicts and pollution are certainly adverse to the growth of seal and sea lion populations, the main deterrent is the physical conflict with man for space. The demand for waterfront recreation, residential development, and industry has grown much faster than the population. As people occupy the beach with their houses, their boats, and their pets, more and more marine mammals are excluded, particularly for the critical activity of pupping, which usually takes place on land.

Clamming, a popular human activity, is heaviest in spring and early summer on beaches exposed at low tide. These are also the optimum breeding areas for seals, but beaches utilized for clamming are unlikely to be suitable for seal or sea lion pupping. Thus by unintentional human actions, seals and sea lions are limited more and more to the less developed areas of the country: Maine, Alaska, and offshore islands. Yet even offshore islands can prove dubious sanctuaries. The monk seal, which has occupied the relatively remote islands of the Windward Chain of the Hawaiian

Islands, has been substantially reduced during the past 20 years, and is now listed as an endangered species. This reduction is probably due in part to military disturbance, though the whole picture is not clear. A recovery team seeking ways to remedy the situation must also consider the possibility of negative impacts resulting from fisheries development.

Threats to Alaska's Seals

The marine mammals of Alaska, notably the northern fur seal, would seem to have less to fear at the moment from such human pressure. In the past two decades, a small colony has also been established on San Miguel Island, one of the California Channel Islands. The vast majority of the northern fur seal population, however, uses the remote Pribilof Islands in the Bering Sea as their breeding and pupping area. While the fur seal was severely depleted twice by exploitation, in the 1820s and again in the early 1900s, the 1911 treaty provided a reprieve. Under careful management, the Bering Sea herd grew rapidly between 1911 and 1956. From 1956 to 1968, a planned reduction of females was carried out to make the herd more productive and at the same time to make less impact on fishery stocks of the North Pacific Ocean. This reduction did not have the expected effect. At the present time the commercial kill of sub-adult males for their fur on St. Paul, the main island, is about half of what it was in the period between 1940 and 1956.

Development of a substantial fishery in the Bering Sea and Gulf of Alaska during the 1950s and 1960s may explain the slowdown in fur seal harvest. Fish catches peaked at just over two million tons in 1971. An estimated standing stock of more than 25 million tons of fish and squid serve as prey for seals and sea lions and also support the fishery. Though in this perspective, overall fishery catches seem small, more significant local effects could result.

The major threat to fur seals, though, comes not from human fishing but from potential developments on their breeding islands. The fur seal rookeries of Alaska occupy St. Paul and St. George Islands — bleak and isolated dots in Bering Sea that were uninhabited by humans prior to their discovery by Bering in 1787. Russians initiated exploitation of the fur seal almost immediately and transplanted Aleuts to perform the manual tasks required. Thus there are now several hundred Pribilof "natives" whose primary industry is fur seal exploitation. However, returns from fur seal operations are too low to support the human populations. At present, federal government activities help subsidize the island economy.

An effort is being made to develop an alternative or additional economic base for the islands. Growth of a small tourist industry might occur but seems unlikely to generate sufficient income to meet the islanders' needs. A fishing industry has been proposed which would require a port and offshore activities. If oil were found in the adjacent basin, additional economic support could be based on such oil exploitation.

Tourists create disturbances which may have a negative but not very significant impact. Activities to develop and maintain a fishing port or oil base with the accompanying offshore activities would undoubtedly have greater negative impact. From the point of view of the seals, the best solution would be to designate the islands as a refuge and to remove the human population. Even if harvesting were maintained using transient workers, pressures to develop the islands would be reduced. Such a solution is neither socially nor politically acceptable. Nor is it clear that further expansion of the fur seal herd would be politically acceptable in view of the animals' impact on fisheries of the Bering Sea and Gulf of Alaska.

The future of the fur seal population, of course, will not be determined by the United States alone. At present, the United States, The Soviet Union, Japan, and Canada are discussing a four-year extension of the existing seal treaty. The treaty bans pelagic sealing, provides for harvest of immature males on land, with sharing of the resulting furs, and calls for research. A broad interpretation of "research" has permitted a moratorium on harvesting on St. George Island since 1973. In other words, the treaty extension will continue the status quo for four more years, a period during which alternative options for the future will be studied. Yet all of these plans could be rendered useless if, as has been proposed, offshore oil production is begun in the early 1980s in the St. George Basin.

Antarctic Seals

Northern hemisphere marine mammals are being displaced by man as we come to use or abuse our coastal and nearshore environment. This is true not only in the United States but also in Europe and Asia. In fact, in these continents exploitation and habitat reduction have severely reduced most marine mammals, again with the exception of remote regions. One group of marine mammals has so far been spared from such a fate: the ice seals of the Antarctic, which are collectively the largest group of marine mammals anywhere.

In fact, estimates have been given that the population of crabeater seals around the Antarctic continent numbers 15 million. It is possible that these and perhaps some others of the Antarctic seals have benefited from the decimation of the great whales. The crabeater seals feed exclusively on krill, other Antarctic seals generally less so. Thus it is quite possible krill not consumed by whales has become more easily available to the seals, which have flourished as a result. In any case, they have been trivially exploited and are, so far, free from competition for space except at the few scattered Antarctic research stations. Though a treaty was signed some years ago to regulate commercial exploitation of these seals, none has seriously developed. At present, such exploitation appears to be uneconomic.

There are two possible threats to these animals: the exploitation by man of krill and the exploitation of mineral resources, particularly oil and gas. While some harvesting of krill is now going on, it is in small quantities compared to that consumed by marine mammals. It also seems likely that large scale human exploitation of krill will be inhibited by economic and technological problems. Additionally the countries that have signed the Antarctic treaty to promote peaceful use of the Antarctic continent (notably the United States, United Kingdom, U.S.S.R., Japan, France and several southern hemisphere countries) have recently negotiated a convention on living marine resources. This document has just been signed and remains to be ratified. If ratification takes place by all or most of the major countries involved, it will place restrictions on krill exploitation at levels that would have a major impact on its dependent species. These countries are also in the initial stages of developing a convention relative to mineral resources. It is too early to tell whether this will be sufficiently restrictive to protect the Antarctic seals from the impacts of such development, or whether such development will be economically feasible in the next few decades.

The remoteness of their habitat from human activities has protected the seals of the Antarctic. No such distance protects a vanishing group of marine mammals known as manatees.

Manatees

The manatee is the only member of the sirenian family living within the continental United States, primarily in Florida, though occasionally ranging farther north in summer. There are also a few in Puerto Rico. The Florida population has been estimated to number about 1,000 though this figure may be somewhat low. Unlike seals and sea lions, manatees are entirely aquatic and do not haul out on land. On the other hand, manatees are found primarily in the coastal environment, either in salt water near shore or the fresh water of adjacent rivers. Thus manatees share with seals and sea lions many of the perils associated with the coast. For example, 335 carcasses were found in salvage surveys of 1974-79, surveys which certainly do not count all dead animals. If the population is only 1,000 animals, such a mortality rate could not be long sustained before the population became extinct. Recoveries have decreased since that time.

Human activities cause a large fraction of observed manatee deaths: injuries from power boat propellers, barge collisions, entrapment in flood control gates, and entanglement in fishing gear. Some deaths are caused by vandalism and/or poaching. Such mortality is critical for a population of such small size. Yet equally serious is the loss of habitat to development or drainage projects.

One development appears superficially to be beneficial to manatees, yet may actually be a hidden danger. In winter they must move south or find warm water refuge. Power plants, by discharging warm water into the sea, have created many new refuges in recent years. But in the extremely cold winter of 1976-77 a Brevard County power plant shut down twice, in January and February.

Though the question of cause and effect cannot be answered absolutely, 19 dead manatees were found in February 1977, the time of the extreme cold.

A variety of actions have been taken to protect the manatee population. These include setting up sanctuaries and restricting power boat speeds. At the same time, a recovery plan has been developed by the Fish and Wildlife Service. Steps are being taken to educate enforcement officers and the public about the threats to the manatee. Research is being initiated and should be continued on habitat needs of these animals as well as ways to mitigate the more severe direct causes of death, especially power boats and flood control structures. Such steps may come soon enough to save the manatee in the short run; in the long run, we must ask if the increasing population and the increasing use of the water environment leave a future for the manatee in Florida — or anywhere.

Cetaceans

Cetaceans include the several species of great whales — blue, fin, gray, humpback, sperm, sei and minke — as well as other whales and a large number of species of dolphins and porpoises. Unlike pinnipeds, cetaceans do not haul out on land or ice and thus would seem to be less affected by man's terrestrial activities. However, some cetaceans *are* found in coastal waters where a serious effect is possible. These include bowhead, gray and humpback, as well as beluga (or white) whales and the harbor porpoise.

Bowhead Whales

The bowhead whale has been hunted by native people in the Arctic for many centuries. It early became an important prey for European commercial whalers who discovered its remote feeding locations in or near the ice in the search for a Northwest or Northeast Passage. Five or six stocks are identified in the different regions of the Arctic. All have been depleted to seriously low levels.

The largest remaining bowhead stock winters in the Bering Sea off Siberia. As the ice opens up in the spring, the herd follows the leads in the ice northward through the Bering Strait past the north slope of Alaska toward its summer feeding area in the Beaufort Sea northwest of the Mackenzie delta in the Canadian Northwest territories. Commercial hunting from 1848 to the early 1900s reduced this stock from perhaps 20,000 to a few hundred.

From time immemorial Eskimos along the Alaskan coast have hunted bowhead whales as the herd migrates northward in the spring and, to a lesser extent, southward in the fall. They still do. In the 1970s, with expanded opportunity to obtain employment elsewhere in Alaska and thereby obtain the funds to purchase whaling equipment, the number of Eskimo whaling expeditions increased sharply. The number of whales captured increased as did the number struck and lost.

The International Whaling Commission's Scientific Committee expressed concern over this increased kill from a stock whose status was very uncertain. Eventually, in 1977, the IWC committee recommended that there be no further taking from the stock. The Commission modified this recommendation to permit continued native subsistence hunting but with quotas on the number retrieved and on the number struck. Eskimos dispute the right of the International Whaling Commission to regulate an aboriginal hunt. Some villagers ignored government regulations in 1980. This controversy has also split the conservation community, with Friends of the Earth and other groups supporting the Eskimos, and others calling for an end to bowhead whaling.

Both Eskimos and conservationists agree on one point: the exploration for and exploitation of oil in waters north of Alaska might have a more serious impact on the whales than the native take. Adverse effects could be caused by noise, seismic booms used in exploration, vessel traffic, and oil spills. All of these possible effects are being studied by the Department of the Interior's Bureau of Land Management as part of the preparation of environmental impact statements.

Litigation over these activities has already occurred and more can be expected in the future. As scientists try to provide relevant data, it will be difficult to determine through laboratory experiments or even field studies whether the effects noted above are negligible or critical. Most probably, they lie between the two extremes. It is very difficult to balance the possible adverse effect on an endangered species and on the native peoples who depend on it against the benefits to be obtained from oil exploitation.

Coastal Threats to Other Cetaceans

Other cetaceans that spend much of their time near the coast include the gray, right, and humpback whales and the beluga or white whale of the Arctic. The beluga whale, hunted more by Canadians than by U.S. citizens, could be affected in the same way as the bowhead whale.

Gray whales migrate along the west coast of North America from their feeding grounds in the Chucksi Sea off Siberia to their mating and calving areas in and near the lagoons of Baja California. In these lagoons they were very vulnerable to exploitation and were twice reduced substantially. Protected since the 1930s, except for native take, mostly by Siberians, the stock has recovered. Today the "hunters" are whale watchers who seek only to observe the gray whales, particularly on the southbound migration past California and during the winter in the lagoons of Baja California. Whether whale-watching boats constitute "harrassment" and could have an adverse effect on these whales is undecided. As whale watching increased in the 1960s off San Diego, more whales apparently migrated offshore out of range of the whale watching boats. On the other hand, we have the phenomenon of the "curious whales" in recent years in San Ignacio Lagoon. These whales not only approach small boats and investigate them; they also permit themselves to be petted and stroked.

The most serious threat to these whales is not from such activities but from industrial and oil development along the coast and in the lagoons. Salt barges appear to have negative effects in Guerro Negro Lagoon, part of the complex that is called Scammon's Lagoon and which is the largest breeding area. Large scale oil development might drive the whales from the lagoons completely. Conservation groups therefore seek to have any such exploitation carried on in such a way as to minimize or avoid affecting the lagoons and the whales.

Humpback and right whales are both coastal species and thus vulnerable to human exploitation. As such, they were seriously depleted in number by past exploitation. The right whales suffered losses decades ago; the humpbacks, since World War II. The numbers of both species are still low: for right whales a few score animals, for humpback whales, several hundreds or thousands. A few humpbacks are still killed in the West Indies and Greenland. A larger number, perhaps 30, are killed annually by entanglement in fishing nets, mostly off Newfoundland.

The Pacific humpback whales, seen frequently in summer off Alaska and in winter off Hawaii, have neither of these problems. Like the gray whale, the Pacific humpback is a subject of whale watching, which may affect it adversely. Some restrictions have been put into effect in Glacier Bay National Monument in Alaska and off Hawaii. Such activities are likely to be much less serious than oil exploitation or exploration. Again, research is being carried out to measure such effects prior to leasing of oil development rights.

Porpoises and Dolphins

Most species of dolphins and porpoise tend to be sufficiently far from the coast to have been little affected by man, except the spotted and spinner dolphins which have been set upon by yellow fin tuna purse seiners of the central eastern Pacific. This kill has been vastly reduced following a series of actions taken by the U.S. Government, the industry and the International Tropical Tuna Commission. Annual kill is now below 25,000 of all species.

However, little is known of the effect of the whole purse seine operation on these dolphins. The process involves motorboats chasing about eight million animals annually and encircling and capturing perhaps five million. Whether a way of efficiently capturing yellow fin tuna can be found that avoids this process is unknown. Some potentially helpful research is underway on methods of aggregating tuna schools other than through their association with dolphins.

One porpoise species is found mostly inshore. Its name, the harbor porpoise, suggests its niche. Yet, because it is a very shy and secretive animal, little is known about its numbers and its reaction to man. Clearly, in the most heavily industrialized and polluted harbors, its niche has been eliminated. But it may still exist in reasonable numbers in less disturbed, enclosed arms of the ocean. Unlike "Flipper" and other bottlenose dolphins of aquaria, the harbor porpoise does not do well in captivity and so has been barely studied.

Environmental and conservation groups have fought many battles in recent years. Some of these have had particular symbolic importance in the continuing struggle for a more liveable world. At the moment, the fight to save the whales and all marine mammals from exploitation is being won, though continuing vigilance remains essential. The fight to save the places where they live is just beginning.

For all but the whales and porpoises of the deep oceans and perhaps the Antarctic seals, the future of marine mammals may depend on human ability to preserve the coastal environment from abuse and on human willingness to share it with the animals.

The
Politics of Pelicans

DANIEL W. ANDERSON
and
FRANKLIN GRESS

DANIEL W. ANDERSON

is Associate Professor in the Department of Wildlife and Fisheries
Biology at the University of California at Davis. He earned
his PhD in Wildlife Ecology and Zoology at the University
of Wisconsin.

His chief research interests are in avian ecology, pollution
ecology, and resource management. He has studied eggshell thinning caused by environmental pollutants, the pharmacodynamics
of pollutants in birds, and fish-piscivore interrelationships, and
has done population studies of marine birds. He has conducted his
research on the Great Lakes, in central Canada, in California,
Peru, the Gulf of California, and Baja California.

FRANKLIN GRESS

is a research associate in the Department of Wildlife and Fisheries
Biology and PhD candidate at the University of California at Davis;
he is also the president of the Bodega Bay Institute of Environmental Education, a non-profit environmental research and
education organization. His research interests are in the areas of
seabird ecology, resource management, and marine pollution
ecology. He has worked on projects in arctic Alaska, Antarctica,
Gulf of California, Central America, as well as in California. He is
presently working on marine bird-fishery interactions and the
biology and conservation of the California Brown Pelican in the
Southern California Bight.

The California brown pelican, its graceful flight a familiar sight as the bird flies over the southern California coast, nests in the Channel Islands off Santa Barbara. Like the canary, which coal miners carried into dark shafts to warn them of noxious gases, the brown pelican has become a warning of dangerous pollutants and other stresses in the marine environment. It was one of the first species to show damage from DDT and other chemical pollutants.

Dr. Daniel P. Anderson, Associate Professor in the Department of Wildlife and Fisheries Biology at the University of California at Davis, and his colleague Franklin Gress, a doctoral candidate in ecology, describe the multiple threats to the pelican's survival. Their scholarly analysis reveals that pelican protection per se has had wide ramifications as efforts to protect the single species served to help protect the whole coastal ecosystem. The task is far from complete; the tools for success still inadequate.

By focusing on a single indicator species in detail, the authors make us aware that efforts to protect even one species inevitably require a much broader approach to environmental protection than the Endangered Species Act, alone, provides. Anderson and Gress argue that a new approach to resource management can save endangered species. This approach encompasses food sources as well as nesting grounds; it is an approach that protects not just a species, but an ecosystem.

THE CALIFORNIA BROWN PELICAN (*Pelecanus occidentalis californicus*) has become a focal point and symbol of efforts to protect not just an endangered species, but offshore wildlife and coastal habitat as well. The disastrous effects of oceanic pollution on brown pelicans nesting in southern California's marine environment has aroused immense public attention. Sympathetic attitudes and concern for the "plight of the pelican" have brought protection that has helped more than just the recovery of the pelican. Public concern has also fostered broader programs and goals for coastal conservation issues that reach far beyond the pelican. Thus, efforts to preserve a single species (or population thereof) may augment and encourage needed actions affecting a wide range of environmental concerns.

Many conservation issues related to brown pelicans are centered in the Channel Islands area off the coast of southern California (figure 1). There, brown pelicans have historically been a stable faunal element. In fact, the native American Chumash name for Anacapa Island, site of California's major brown pelican breeding colony, was "P'i awa phew," the "house of pelicans" [11].* The California Channel Islands and associated flora and fauna are among the crown jewels of California's native natural resources. Despite their proximity to highly urbanized coastal southern California, many of these islands remain essentially wild. Because of its uniqueness, however, the area is well known and well studied by scientists [48]. These resources represent a national treasure of cultural and natural history. Like other coastal regions close to major metropolitan areas, the Channel Islands are vulnerable to human pressures from recreation, tourism, and commercial exploitation. Not unexpectedly, then, within this scenario of both development and preservation, conflicts and controversy must arise.

We see the interrelatedness of all parts of the marine ecosystem whenever we study any one part in depth. Although our discussion will center on the California brown pelican, a list of issues on which the preservation of this one endangered species touches reads like the table of contents to a book on coastal environmental concerns. Focusing on brown pelican conservation, we will examine the following issues: 1) preservation of a genetic entity as related to the Endangered Species Act; 2) the use of the offshore zone as a dumping ground for pollutants; 3) potential conflicts over resources sought by both humans and marine wildlife; 4) international complications of preserving and managing a migratory resource; 5) offshore oil development and its potential adverse effects on marine wildlife; 6) potential environmental impacts of the Space Shuttle; and 7) island and offshore sanctuary and refuge establishment. Most of these issues are interrelated, but the one important thread binding them together in the southern California marine environment is the conservation of brown pelicans. It will

*The numbers in brackets correspond to references listed in the Reference section in the back of the book under the heading "The Politics of Pelicans and Coastal Protection," p. 175.

be our goal here to review briefly these environmental issues from our viewpoints as scientists and conservationists.

"One of the penalties of an ecological education is that one lives alone in a world of wounds."

Aldo Leopold [37]

The California Brown Pelican

The California brown pelican is a distinctly named subspecies representing a unique genetic entity and is the western form of a much more widespread species [47]. The populations associated with southern California nest mostly at two island groups: Anacapa Islands in U.S. waters and Islas Coronados in Mexican waters. There is evidence that breeding pelicans can interchange between the two island groups, but these two colonies combined represent the northernmost stable and consistent population segments of *P. o. californicus* [10]. The population is "peripheral" in the geographical sense: that is, it exists near the periphery of the species' range. Peripheral status does not mean that such populations are less viable, but it does mean that natural selection pressures might be different from those in the more central populations [40].

Not more than a decade past, breeding populations of brown pelicans were in danger of imminent local extirpation off southern California [58, 4]. Colonies at Anacapa Island, Los Coronados, and perhaps one or two colonies farther south were reduced to about ten percent of historical numbers [10, 4]. The subspecies itself, however, has never been in danger of extinction; its range extends well south into western Mexico (figure 2) [47]. Because of large influxes of brown pelicans from Mexico, mostly from the Gulf of California, the presence of pelicans was never threatened off California's coast. Thus uninformed observers have concluded that concern for brown pelicans off southern California was not justified. Yet early surveys of breeding populations in the Southern California Bight indicated that whole portions of the northern population were in danger of being lost [57, 53, 35].

The Endangered Species Act

The California brown pelican was included on the list of Endangered Species in 1969. Revision of the act in 1973 gave the U.S. Fish and Wildlife Service the needed authority to effect conservation measures for "species" designated as "threatened" or "endangered" [59]. Amendments to the act in 1978 and 1979 provide the following new procedures: 1) public hearings and meetings, 2) economic analysis, 3) inclusion of critical habitat with the listing, and 4) exemption processes under Section 7. Some relevant terminology is defined:

> *"species"* — "any species, any subspecies, and any smaller taxonomic units of plant or (vertebrate) animal, and also any viable population-segment thereof."
> *"endangered"* — "those species in danger of extinction throughout all or a significant portion of their range."
> *"threatened"* — "those species which are likely to become endangered within the foreseeable future."

Endangered species can be reverted to "threatened" status if their population begins to recover, or endangerment can be retained if a species' recovery is imperiled. Threatened status generally involves the same protection as endangered status, although it gives more management options to local wildlife management agencies. In some cases, especially relating to harvested or hunted populations such as the American alligator (*Alligator mississippiensis*), it has sometimes been more realistic to change to threatened status.

To illustrate the importance of the Endangered Species Act to U.S. wildlife conservation and to the brown pelican in California coastal conservation, we cite a 1980 report by the U.S. Fish and Wildlife Service [60]. The report describes 49 important California "fish and wildlife habitats" in order to: 1) identify relict areas (those left relatively undisturbed by man) and their threats, 2) identify as far as practical small ecosystems that are threatened, rather than individual components, and 3) eventually stimulate a large variety of protective measures. A statement of basic philosophy affirmed that "the vanguard of the species preservation effort must be aimed at the maintenance of viable ecosystem units." Of 12 coastal habitats cited, six specifically mentioned brown pelicans and seven mentioned other endangered species. Thirty-seven upland or freshwater habitats included 17 instances where endangered species were mentioned specifically [60]. It should be clear that, just as with the wildlife refuge system (funded largely through duck stamp revenues), many non-target species benefit from the Endangered Species Act. The overall result can be ecosystem preservation.

Under the Endangered Species Act guidelines, then, it was necessary to show that the California brown pelican was a viable subspecies and that it was endangered in some places within its range. Our work in Mexico and California indicates that the northern population segments — those in the Channel Islands area — are somewhat unique as well, and that southern California's pelicans *do* represent a formerly "viable population segment."

It is likely that genetic selection occurs most intensely at the species' range periphery; such populations might represent less variable but perhaps more specialized genetic packages [40]. From this perspective, the potential loss of one or two colonies on the range periphery may be a highly significant loss to the species. The conclusions to be reached from such facts are quite opposite from the attitude often expressed that since there are plenty of pelicans in Mexico, why concern ourselves with the relatively few in California, which are on the range periphery anyway and are insignificant to the species as a whole?

As migratory seabirds, pelicans transcend international boundaries. The endangered population segment extends into northwestern Baja California where some of the southern colonies (such as Isla Todos Santos and Isla San Martín) have either been much reduced in number or no longer exist [35]. A 1972 amendment to the 1936 Migratory Bird Treaty Act fortunately includes brown pelicans. Mexican wildlife authorities have taken steps to protect seabird nesting colonies and islands in the Gulf of California, at least on the lawbooks [7]. Conservation of the total subspecies will not be possible without international cooperation, and there are signs that a much larger proportion of the California brown pelican may soon be threatened [5]. Perhaps for this reason, some have suggested that the entire subspecies be designated as threatened [56]. Because of international uncertainties, it becomes even more important that we protect southern California breeding populations as best we can.

Ecologists, behaviorists, and geneticists are beginning to identify with great precision local units such as "populations." The term is used here to mean: a group of individuals that share life history characteristics and thus are genetically more alike among themselves than among individuals of other similar groups. Provisions to protect the tule goose (*Anser albifrons gambelli*) and Canada goose (*Branta canadensis*) are classic examples of specific management responses to identifiable populations [13]. Because Canada goose management is complicated by hunting as well, it is a goal to manage by population-unit [49]. Such a process often advances as follows: 1) define and understand a population through extensive research, 2) which generates concern by policy makers, 3) which in turn generates conservation action. Regarding the status of the brown pelican throughout its range (including Florida, Texas, etc.), one can argue logically against granting endangered status to the entire species, when not all populations are endangered [56]. It might be more realistic to subdivide the species into logical management units while still retaining the usefulness of the Endangered Species Act. A broadscale approach based on the technicalities of taxonomic status of an entire species or subspecies should be abandoned. The use of large geographical scale management units is not where wildlife management is going today.

A five-year review of the endangered species status for brown pelicans is underway. Changing the brown pelican's legal status to "threatened" or removing it entirely from the list of endangered species now would seem only to undermine the broader aspects of pelican conservation. Relinquishment of authority needed to help ensure both the recovery of the brown pelican population and the broader needs of other California marine wildlife would be premature and perhaps even irresponsible at this point.

This issue, if taken in wider context, means to the conservationist that perhaps newer and broader federal and state laws are needed to bolster the Endangered Species Act. Similarly, the states need more aid in implementing stronger, more effective nongame, nonendangered species programs. The Nongame Fish and Wildlife Conservation Act of 1980 may be a step in the right direction. We need to supplement and bolster the Endangered Species Act rather than to undermine it.

Because of actions taken in the last decade or so, there is good evidence that southern California breeding populations of brown pelicans are on their way to recovery [10]. Recent pelican conservation measures, though minimal, may truly represent a *limited* success story in seabird and endangered species conservation. However, the recovery itself may now be at risk because of offshore pollution, oil exploration, conflicts over the fish on which pelicans feed, and other problems.

One of the most desired goals of wildlife conservationists is to anticipate problems and to take action *before* damage to wildlife occurs. Conservation can never be truly successful unless it is anticipatory. All too often the damage is done before anyone knows the problem exists. As we gain new insights in protecting wildlife, new and more sophisticated strategies will be required.

The situation with widespread DDT pollution was such a case. The after-the-fact nature of that problem was not so much a success story as was popularly believed, because much of the damage had occurred before the problem was recognized and acted upon. The lessons learned from the DDT problem apply to issues we discuss here regarding wildlife conservation in general. Resource policy makers must be challenged to recognize that large-scale and appropriate research is necessary and that its results should be integrated "at the appropriate time into resource planning, or [they should] admit that short term goals are their only interest and that rational planning is beyond them" [36]. Issues like these are extremely controversial, and it is often most difficult to convince those who are doing the damage that a problem might exist [31].

The southern California marine environment (including coastal marshes and islands), from a wildlife and wildlife habitat viewpoint, should perhaps be considered as "endangered." It may be too much of a risk to rely so heavily on a few species! Yet had it not been for the Endangered Species Act, brown pelican recovery would probably not have been as rapid or as certain. Until a more balanced and wider-scope approach toward all wildlife in the off-shore area is adopted, it seems that endangered status of the pelican can benefit the cause of general wildlife conservation in offshore areas of southern California. Unfortunately, favorable attitudes toward haphazard developments seem to be popular on the assumption that "minimal" damage will occur, or that the resource is not as important as the proposed projects, or that impacts will occur on an "expendable" portion of the "species." Are any populations really expendable?

> "We console ourselves with the comfortable fallacy that a single museum-piece will do, ignoring the clear dictum of history that a species must be saved *in many places* if it is to be saved at all."
>
> Aldo Leopold [37]

Offshore Pollution

Severe contamination of coastal ecosystems almost always results in detrimental physiological and ecological impacts on fish and wildlife. This has been well documented in California's coastal marine environment. High concentrations of chlorinated hydro-carbons in marine food webs—particularly DDE, an environmentally stable metabolite of DDT—were associated with a number of biological disruptions first observed in the late 1960's and early 1970's [50, 52, 38]. The Peregrine falcon (*Falco peregrinus*), for example, had largely disappeared as a breeding bird along the California coast [30]. Brown pelicans and double-crested cormorants (*Phalacrocorax auritus*) breeding on the Channel Islands and along the Baja California coast suffered nearly complete reproductive failures due to excessive thinning of eggshells [35, 51, 27, 3]. A high incidence of premature births and pup mortality was also observed among California sea lions (*Zalophus californicus*) breeding on southern California islands [19, 25]. All of these events were associated with high levels of chlorinated hydrocarbon pollutants.

Severe eggshell thinning resulted in lowered reproductive success in the more contaminated populations, such as brown pelicans and double-crested cormorants breeding in the Southern California Bight [53, 27]. Levels of chlorinated hydrocarbon residues in eggs of these two species revealed the extent and pattern of extreme contamination by DDE of the California and Baja California coastal marine environments [35, 53, 27, 3]. As a result it was found that the major source of the DDT in the sea was effluent from a Los Angeles county sewage system, which received liquid wastes from a DDT manufacturing plant [6, 38, 53]. Subsequent disposal of these wastes in a sanitary landfill resulted in a sharp decline of DDT input into the sea from this sewage system [51, 3]. Thereafter, levels of these compounds decreased in brown pelicans and other organisms in the Southern California Bight [3, 51, 55]. Reproductive success increased in brown pelicans and in double-crested cormorants as levels of DDE decreased [27, 3].

Waterbirds, particularly those of the orders Pelecaniformes and Ciconiiformes (herons, ibises, egrets) are excellent indicators of environmental contamination in coastal and estuarine systems [44, 45]. The brown pelican became the key indicator species of southern California coastal pollution and a rallying point in the attempts to eliminate or reduce pollution levels there. This is the most well-known and perhaps the most emotional southern California issue involving the brown pelican [18]. It has become a classic example of adverse effects of oceanic pollution on a wildlife population. While the problems from DDT have lessened, other substances in addition to DDT that are toxic to seabirds continue to enter the marine ecosystem.

DDT pollution problems in southern California coastal waters have not been eliminated. Instead, an acute situation has become chronic, and other potential environmental impacts (such as other forms of pollution, human activities, and even normal environmental variations that cause populations to fluctuate) now have the potential to attain importance in affecting pelican population status and well-being. The encouraging aspect of the DDT pollution problem was that something was done to help eliminate it. Even minimal and peripheral measures actually seemed to make a difference by reducing some of the perturbations.

All this sets the stage for considerations of future environmental impact evaluation and the value of brown pelicans as indicator species in southern California. It *is* worthwhile to seek biological data and relevant information on an appropriate situation such as this, and then to seek actions through administrative channels. The ideal goal, of course, would be to make this system anticipatory. The impact of pollutants on pelicans, and thus on the southern California marine environment, has helped alert society to some of the broader implications and degradations of the natural coastal ecosystem.

Resource-Use Conflicts

Brown pelicans feed predominantly on northern anchovies (*Engraulis mordax*) off southern California; their reproductive rates today vary with variations in anchovy availability [9, 28]. Therefore the management of either of these two resources cannot be dealt with separately [8]. Obviously there are ramifications for other species of wildlife as well [34]. A major competitor to pelicans (and other marine wildlife as well) for the fish resource is the commercial fishery. Although few fishermen believe that pelicans actually jeopardize and diminish their harvest, the conflict between commercial fisheries and pelican utilization of a common resource — anchovies — is symptomatic of the pervasive issue of native resources versus exploitation.

In terms of marine bird conservation, protection and assurances of undisturbed nesting sites are important for long-term viability [7]. However, adequate protection of food supplies is equally necessary [5]. Food supplies often are difficult to identify, let alone manage, in complex ecosystems. Protection of nesting sites is much more straightforward and is usually the main action taken by conservation agencies when "management plans" are implemented. Such protection represents an early but essential step in the evolution of a conservation program.

It is more difficult to deal with food supplies, which are not only mobile, but are desired by humans, seabirds, marine mammals, and predatory fish. As fish resources change (through changes in species compositions and abundances, change in potential prey behavior, etc.) so do critical or "key-industry" prey species from the perspective of a seabird. Thus, management must be flexible and provide for continuous monitoring so that necessary action can be taken when changes require it. Management is thus nearly impossible on a truly scientific basis, where adequate data input takes an enormous amount of time and money. A conservative approach to proposed impacts, therefore, becomes essential to ensure that damage or imbalances in the natural system do not occur or that they at least remain minimal. This approach should go hand-in-hand with as sophisticated an understanding as available scientific techniques make feasible (the more scientific data, the better). Society also dictates economic, political and social benefit factors to resource managers, but these considerations can only be secondary to the prime goal of balanced and perpetual resource conservation.

Under the Fisheries Conservation and Management Act of 1976, responsible agencies are required to formulate management plans on all important commercial species of fish in order to ensure: 1) optimum yield, with 2) guaranteed perpetuation of that resource, and 3) minimal impact to the rest of the system that contains that resource (i.e., to minimize the ecological effects of harvest). The Endangered Species Act and Marine Mammal Protection Act prohibit any environmental alterations that would affect the status or recovery of an endangered species or an alteration of optimum carrying capacity for marine mammals. Some conflict is inevitable because a significant impact through intensive management to achieve optimum yield and resource perpetuation does not mesh with the Endangered Species Act or the Marine Mammal Act. Also, because assessment of impact on an ecosystem is largely ignored until an effect is proved, managers often rely again on indicator or otherwise important species.

One of the first management plans on the West Coast under the Fisheries Conservation Management Act, and a landmark in itself, is the Anchovy Management Plan prepared in 1978 by the Pacific Fisheries Management Council, a multiagency group consisting of fish biologists and fishery management specialists [46]. The plan provides several harvest options that range from very conservative to liberal (depending on resource-use viewpoint). The options are chosen by appointed commissioners — in California by the California Fish and Game Commission — with advice from federal and state agencies. The Commission listens to all viewpoints and interest groups at hearings, then attempts to make the most balanced decisions. This is often not easy to do.

A major conflict is the multiple-use aspect of the anchovy fishery. How can a basically virgin resource be converted to optimum yield and yet satisfy the needs of all users, including wildlife? Multiple-use may be the impossible dream without concessions from one or more users, especially in a highly political system [39]. It seems that with a high-yield goal for one resource within a complex system, something must give. In southern California, it is not hard to imagine that intensive anchovy harvests could result, for example, in reduced populations of seabirds and the large predatory fish sought by sport and commercial fishermen [24].

One major problem not yet addressed in any management plan (which becomes more complex and unwieldy with involvement of more species) is that predators and non-human consumers are all thrown together. Off southern California the abundance of anchovies varies considerably from year to year, but the Anchovy Management Plan seeks to ensure a constant "forage reserve" for wild consumers of about one million tons, a figure which is considered to be about one-fourth of maximum abundance. Only a proportion of the biomass over the forage reserve level may be taken by commercial fishermen. There is good evidence that the breeding success of brown pelicans in the California Bight may be highly dependent on the abundance of anchovies over a large geographical area [8, 9].

Even if the anchovy is replaced by some other species, the principles are the same: marine bird population status may depend on the abundance of surface fishes in the system. There are some suggestions that more moderate commercial harvests than proposed and perhaps even the closing of some areas to fishing, are needed to ensure that pelican recovery continues. Sport fishery interests share this concern over excessive anchovy harvests because the gamefish they seek also feed on anchovies [23]. This interest group wants insurance that game fish (usually the large predators) will not be affected by an intensive commercial harvest. Because of decreases in anchovy abundance from about 1976 to 1979, the Anchovy Management Plan has not yet been fully tested [8].

When federal action is planned that could affect a species protected by the Endangered Species Act, the agency must first consult with the Fish and Wildlife Service and reach a mutual agreement. This process is referred to as "Section 7 consultation." In the case of brown pelicans, this means that the potential impacts of any proposal to increase anchovy harvests, or, for that matter, to alter the brown pelican food supply, need to be considered. However, there are potential conflicts in the goals of the Endangered Species Act and the Fisheries Conservation and Management Act. The importance of the actions taken by the responsible agencies depends in part on the degree of protection the brown pelican has under the Endangered Species Act. To date, the California Department of Fish and Game has taken an encouragingly conservative stand [23].

At this point, two major weaknesses in the entire management and monitoring system seem to be the estimate of anchovy biomass and the need for much more data on fish and wildlife consumers in the system. In the late summer of 1980, mostly because of discrepancies in federal and state biomass estimates, the commission adopted a policy of limited anchovy harvest that was much more conservative than that allowed by the Anchovy Management Plan. This put the state agency and the National Marine Fisheries Service into a potential conflict. Fortunately, winter 1980 catches improved, and an open agency confrontation was averted.

A "Catch 22" in this entire system is the international nature of the anchovy and pelican resources [46, 5]. Mexico now harvests more anchovies than we do, and in recent years, a greater and greater proportion of the allowable take has been allocated to Mexican fisheries. Between 1970 and 1979, U.S. catch varied between 11,000 and 156,000 short tons (1978 and 1979 were 11,000 and 52,000 shorts tons respectively); Mexico's catch has risen steadily from 6,000 to 208,000 short tons [42]. No matter what is done in U.S. waters, therefore, anchovies and consequently pelicans and other wildlife may be affected. Thus the entire situation may be out of our hands. While Mexican biologists are sympathetic to international fishery management plans, their politicians, like ours, are usually not. Mexico's President Jose

Lopez Portillo in December 1980 withdrew his country's obligations for several provisions of bilateral fishing treaties with the United States.

Decisions by other countries may force a unilateral approach to our own management of southern California offshore resources. More dangerously, it could lead to the attitude: "Why do all this just so foreign fisheries can take the resource; why not get all we can for ourselves?" The Pacific Fisheries Management Council has its work cut out for it; the Mexican complications may be the most pressing problem facing these fishery resource managers in the near future [23]. Ironically, the well-being of California's brown pelicans may depend on how well our federal agencies negotiate international fishery management programs. Even so, we have the capability to act responsibly in our own waters.

At present, with limited funding and limited interest for more ecosystem-oriented approaches (which are long-term and time-consuming), one-species, simple systems (simple only in relation to more complex systems) will be studied as indicators of the broader aspects of ecosystems off southern California. Eventually single-species plans like the Anchovy Management Plan and the California Brown Pelican Recovery Plan may have to be changed as they are incorporated into more community-oriented plans [24, 29, 46]. We need to begin dealing with offshore marine resources in their natural context rather than as systems reduced to "mono-culture" status to maximize the production of a single component, whether it be anchovies, pelicans, sportsfish, or some other resource. Until such approaches become feasible, however, we must continue to rely on indicator species such as the brown pelican and anchovy to monitor and thus protect the overall health of our coastal zone. Despite all the hinted failings of the system as it exists (we would guess the largest failing to be the philosophical differences in what a resource is *meant* to be used for), none better seems to exist.

Offshore Oil Development

The Santa Barbara Channel for a number of years has been the site of offshore drilling and, in recent years, of intensive oil exploration. The hazard to marine wildlife resources posed by these activities is enormous. As a result of the 1969 Santa Barbara Channel oil spill, we know the potential of oil well blowouts and the dangers of oil spills in this area.

Before expansion of offshore petroleum activities, the Outer Continental Shelf Office of the Bureau of Land Management conducted extensive studies of marine resources in the Southern California Bight. These investigations, performed from 1975 to 1979, were to establish a baseline and to determine "areas of concern" — those places that include viable marine resources which require special consideration and protection and might therefore be excluded from petroleum drilling operations. Baseline studies were undertaken to determine both present status of marine resources and natural variability over a period of time as a measure of future impacts. The baseline studies of marine wildlife in the Channel Islands region provided the first systematic assessment of marine bird populations undertaken in that area [32, 33].

In the summer of 1980, a single situation arose in which petroleum operations posed a potential threat to the Anacapa Island colony and which illustrated other potential future conflicts [16]. Chevron U.S.A., Inc., sought to place an exploratory well just 5.7 miles north of Anacapa Island in the Santa Barbara Channel. The proposed well would have been located within the buffer zone of the northbound sea lane and within the six-mile zone delineating the Channel Islands Marine Sanctuary. Under regulations implementing the Federal Coastal Management Act, federal agencies ". . . cannot grant a permit for any activity described in an Outer Continental Shelf Plan of Exploration until the California Coastal Commission concurs with the certification by the oil company applicant that the activity is consistent with the California Coast Management Program or determines that the activity has no effect on the coastal zone" [43].

In a lengthy document submitted to the California Coastal Commission, Chevron characterized the Anacapa Island brown pelican population as a peripheral colony with chronic low productivity that had been so severely impacted by man over the years that there was little hope for long-term viability [17]. Chevron further argued that the presence or absence of this colony would make little difference to the brown pelican population as a whole. The company painted a picture of a pelican colony so decimated by so many other human and natural disruptions that the impact of an oil spill would be of little further consequence. Further, Chevron dismissed the importance of the Santa Barbara Channel as a feeding area for pelicans breeding on Anacapa despite the fact that it is where pelicans primarily feed while nesting. In fact, aerial surveys of the Channel showed the general location of the proposed well to have one of the highest densities of pelicans at sea [28]. Adult pelicans incubating eggs or tending young commonly feed near the colony, particularly in the Channel just north of Anacapa. Obviously the pelicans depend on close-by food resources (30-50 km. from the colony and closer) while incubating eggs or caring for young [10, 28].

Chevron also stated that pelicans avoid oil spills. Often, however, we have seen pelicans and their eggs fouled with oil. We do not have specific information on how an oil spill would affect pelican reproductive success or population dynamics since we have not witnessed or studied the effects of a spill on a pelican breeding area. We are aware of pelican mortality due to oil fouling in the Gulf of California on two occasions, and the literature contains numerous references on sublethal effects of oil fouling on other species. Contrary to Chevron's statement, pelicans certainly do not avoid surface oil. As young-of-the-year pelicans fledge, they often congregate in large numbers on the water surface near the colony or on rocks along Anacapa's shore. Young pelicans do not at first range far from the colony. If an oil spill occurred during this time and washed up on shore, the impact would be very detrimental to young pelicans and probably would cause some mortality. The risk of oil to pelicans is not limited just to the breeding season. In the fall and winter when pelicans are not breeding, thousands of migrant birds from Mexican colonies flood the southern California coast where they feed extensively until they return south [4, 14]. They, too, could be greatly affected by a major oil spill.

Chevron maintained that the chance of a spill was ". . . so remote it's not worth considering" and furthermore stated that a spill would be only a "minimal" threat to pelicans. However, the Coastal Commission decided that the location of the well in the buffer zone of a major sea lane was a hazard to ship traffic. In August, 1980, the Coastal Commission ruled that the potential of a large spill from a possible collision, the vulnerability of the pelican nesting colony, and the danger to the Island Channel Marine Sanctuary was too great a risk. Application was therefore denied. This was the first time the California Coastal Commission had acted to prevent placement of an offshore well. Concern for pelicans proved to be a powerful factor in asserting a more cautious approach to resource development. Unfortunately, the current Administration plans accelerated oil development, often in sensitive areas and against the wishes of Californians.

The Space Shuttle

At Vandenberg and Edwards Air Force Bases, near Santa Barbara and inland in the desert, respectively, the U.S. Air Force is planning West Coast launch and recovery sites for the U.S. Space Shuttle. Launches will present hazards as yet unknown to all wildlife in the area. Each launch will set off sonic booms and perhaps other phenomena potentially injurious to wildlife. Landings over the Channel Islands area may be more frequent but with perhaps less hazardous sonic booms.

The parties involved in resolving resource conflicts here are two federal agencies mandated by the Endangered Species Act to protect wildlife resources — superficially an ideal situation. But is it? The U.S. Fish and Wildlife Service is a David compared to the Goliath U.S. Air Force, and the Space Shuttle is so high a national priority that wildlife managers may be forced to follow classic precedent and sacrifice yet another wildlife resource. Ideally, priority goals should be attained with little or no damage to wildlife, although environmental impact assessments all too often dismiss too many possibilities of hazard if no direct contradictory data are already available [20]. One should take the most conservative viewpoint, even if it might be damaging to the proposed activity. It would be a small miracle if the Space Shuttle proceeded without some impact on pelicans and other wildlife, yet it would be foolish to believe that wildlife conservation could halt a project such as this.

Data on effects on wildlife of aircraft overpressures — sonic booms of the magnitude expected for the Space Shuttle — along both launch and return paths are generally not available [22]. Apparently, little has been done to answer such questions. A major short-term result of this controversy may be a weakening of the Endangered Species Act itself as public attitudes swing against a strict application of the Act. The title of a news article in a scientific journal aptly summarizes the popular attitude: "Brown Pelican Threat to Space Shuttle" [21]. The issue, as it affects the Endangered Species Act, is reminiscent of the Tellico Dam controversy. There, the status of the snail darter (*Percina tanasi*), a three-inch fish (an endangered gene package, nonetheless), "threatened" an entire government project.

Arguing that the Space Shuttle would not "put the whole species at risk," one reporter made the following misdirected statement: "Such an argument could well receive a more sympathetic hearing from an arbitration committee, able to bring broader social and economic factors into consideration, than by the Department of the Interior, whose judgment on the potential threat of a project would be based on biological and ecological grounds" [21]. If the Interior Department, through the Fish and Wildlife Service, is not the responsible resource agency and could make decisions conciliatory to impactors, then who would speak for the resource?

In southern California other species of wildlife — such as marine mammals, burrow and cavity nesting seabirds, and surface-nesting seabirds — may be in greater jeopardy than brown pelicans. The sonic boom "footprints" from the Shuttle launch would be about two p.s.f. (pounds per square foot) at Anacapa Island, where brown pelicans nest [20, 22]. That is, the sonic boom there would be approximately similar to the sound of a high speed jet aircraft, a sound which is not uncommon in the area, although nobody really knows if present noises are harmful to wildlife. At the San Miguel Island area, where a majority of southern California pinnipeds and a large number of nesting seabirds other than brown pelicans are found, sonic booms could reach as high as 25 p.s.f. [20, 22]. To put these figures in context, it has been estimated that sonic booms of seven p.s.f. can cause inner ear damage; projections for the San Miguel Island area are almost four times that intensity [41].

Among the effects these sonic disturbances might be expected to have on birds, marine mammals, and other wildlife are: 1) Nesting birds, startled by loud sounds, may leave their nests in panic, exposing eggs and fledglings to predators and exposure. 2) California sea lions and other pinnipeds may panic, a situation in which pups are susceptible to trampling by adults. 3) Habitat damage could be especially detrimental at Prince Island, a small islet off San Miguel Island, and one of the most important seabird colony areas in California [33]. 4) Actual physical damage to the inner ears of birds and mammals has been mentioned [22]. 5) Mass reproductive failures due to less intense sonic booms have been suggested in other bird species [12].

Unnatural disturbances to nesting seabirds, caused by many potential factors, have detrimental effects manifested mostly through losses of nest contents [7]. The actual physical damage to eggs or developing embryos from sonic booms is not believed a significant hazard, although more data are needed [22]. In a study near Kennedy International Airport, however, supersonic aircraft caused more disturbance and damage to both roosting and resting herring gulls (*Larus argentatus*) than subsonic aircraft [15].

The long-term nature of the Space Shuttle program, which is expected to be active at least through 1991, means that wildlife conservation problems will need to be anticipated early. Monitoring should be continual and mitigating measures should be taken where necessary and truly practical. While only six launches in the ten-year period are anticipated to be especially hazardous to Channel Islands wildlife, some returns of the craft to earth — as many as 18 a year — will produce two-plus p.s.f. sonic footprints somewhere in the area [22]. Perhaps the true hazards of such landings will be negligible, but they will not be known until after some sonic boom impacts, which means that the wildlife resources themselves will become the experimental subjects. Unfortunately, the monitoring of activities such as these often become the only way wildlife managers can determine hazards to the resource, an after-the-fact procedure that seems to be almost standard. In such a system, early monitoring becomes necessary so that future losses can be anticipated and averted, or at least minimized. To date, we see no such suggestions coming from the responsible agencies. Rather, the strategy seems to be: 1) downplay the potential hazards, and 2) use political tactics to undermine the Endangered Species Act in anticipation that removal of brown pelicans from the list will release the agencies from some impact responsibilities. We suspect that a major weakness today in any impact evaluation to relieve the agencies of mitigation responsibilities is lack of data rather than lack of effect, or perhaps lack of interest or concern.

Island and Offshore Sanctuaries and Refuges

The concept of offshore sanctuaries and island refuges is increasingly important to wildlife survival as development, use, and exploitation of coastal zones accelerate. Goals are not only to protect breeding areas of marine birds, but also to protect nearshore waters adjacent to feeding areas associated with coastal and island-colony sites. Offshore waters are important to seabirds for feeding, raising young, staging and resting during migration, and for wintering. Open ocean as wildlife habitat might at first seem a strange concept, but for marine birds and for some species of waterfowl, the quality of these waters determines their welfare, and as habitat they are every bit as important as breeding areas. Offshore refuges are especially important in protecting feeding areas; in fact, providing protection zones might be the only means of securing many coastal areas in which seabirds feed. Moreover, such zones provide protection of the food resource itself.

Seabird colonies, particularly those on exposed cliff faces rising from the sea, and those on accessible islands, are highly vulnerable to human disturbance, whether from direct approach, loud and sudden sounds, aircraft or boats. A low-flying helicopter approaching a colony at close range, for example, can cause hundreds or even thousands of birds to leave their nests. When pelicans or cormorants are flushed from nests by disturbance, the greatest danger is from gulls or ravens which quickly prey upon eggs or small young left in untended nests [35, 36]. Whole colonies can be completely deserted in the face of such devastating, disturbance-caused predation. Visits by tourists, educational groups, fishermen, and boaters have caused serious disruptions to pelican colonies on the Channel Islands and on the west coast of Baja California [26, 7]. Unfortunately, seabirds are usually highly visible and conspicuous at their colony sites and tend to draw attention. Thus disturbance-related reproductive failures are probably not too uncommon occurrences at seabird colonies throughout the world.

The Endangered Species Act provides for the protection of "critical habitat," which in the case of the brown pelican includes both open ocean and coastal waters. How does one determine the extent of open ocean needed by a bird like the brown pelican? Seabirds are very mobile creatures and they range long distances. If a boundary is to be determined for a marine sanctuary to protect certain species of seabirds, it is not possible to include all the waters utilized by those species. The few studies available suggest that water depth may be the most realistic boundary determinant. However, for offshore sanctuaries a distance that has been used or suggested most often as a boundary is six miles seaward, a boundary which is arbitrary, but which seems reasonable and justified until better data are available [43, 2]. Feeding sites can be protected within such a boundary and it is practical as a management unit.

The National Oceanic and Atmospheric Administration (NOAA), in creating the Channel Islands Marine Sanctuary, established a six-mile buffer from which petroleum operations were prohibited [43]. In this instance, six miles were believed to provide some time and distance for breakup of oil discharges before they reached near-shore communities, but more important, such a zone would increase the available response time for at-sea cleanup and oil-spill containment. The zone would also provide enough distance to reduce visual and acoustic disturbances of petroleum development which may affect marine mammals, seabirds, and the aesthetic qualities of the islands [43].

The Channel Islands Marine Sanctuary was established by NOAA under the Marine Protection, Research and Sanctuaries Act of 1972. In one of his last acts in office, President Carter approved the sanctuary in December, 1980. The Sanctuary was created to preserve the marine resources of the waters surrounding the northern Channel Islands (Anacapa, Santa Cruz, Santa Rosa, and San Miguel) and Santa Barbara Island. The sanctuary extends six nautical miles seaward. Sanctuary status regulates potentially damaging human-related activities, the discharge of contaminants, alteration of and construction on the seabed, aircraft intrusion, and operation of nonfishing and nonrecreational vessels. The designation "provides a formal institutional recognition of the national significance of the resources of this site and focuses, over the long term, on the range of actions necessary to preserve these resources" [43]. It is hoped that management of the marine resources within the sanctuary will complement the management of the Channel Islands National Park and will provide a focus for coordination of local and federal agency regulatory actions.

We do not yet know how the sanctuary will affect brown pelicans, but it is hoped that it will at least prevent aircraft disturbances and that it will protect pelicans from oil industry accidents —although of course oil spills do not respect sanctuary boundaries. The major value of the marine sanctuary is that it has delineated a protective zone for all Channel Islands marine wildlife. However, that protection is not complete for there is little protection for the food resource—the fish on which marine birds feed. Careful coordination of management plans into a unified approach by all involved agencies is essential for the success of the sanctuary. Inter-agency conflicts could undermine the sanctuary concept and render it useless. A more direct threat to the sanctuary emerged in 1981 when the new Administration began to consider opening the sanctuary area to oil operations. Such action would nullify much of the value of the sanctuary.

The Channel Islands National Monument was created in 1938 and became Channel Islands National Park in 1980. Prior to May 15, 1978, the National Park Service had jurisdiction of the waters surrounding Santa Barbara and Anacapa Islands one mile seaward. On that date the U.S. Supreme Court restored jurisdiction to the State of California. This decision greatly altered management policies and regulations, particularly with regard to commercial and sport fishing. The Park Service had developed a management plan over many years to ensure the continued protection and preservation of a unit of unaltered and unique marine environment. This most often involved stringent regulation of commercial fishing. The Park Service zone of jurisdiction certainly did not provide a sanctuary per se, but it did serve to protect the marine life therein as much as possible considering the heavy public use of the area.

When the State of California gained jurisdiction, it seemed unprepared for the responsibility. Commercial fishing interests rushed to harvest what they could, as fast as they could. The situation looked bleak. At the end of May 1978, the California Fish and Game Commission declared a moratorium on fishing in these waters until a plan could be developed and implemented. Ecological reserves were created on the two islands, but protection of the marine resources fell short of what it had been under National Park Service jurisdiction.

One of our chief concerns in the transfer of authority was how to best protect pelicans, their food supplies, and the offshore habitat. We proposed an offshore protective zone closed to trawling and net fishing activities three miles seaward around Anacapa. We felt that such a zone would give the pelicans a buffer zone for feeding during the breeding season and would offer protection for the food resource itself, although pelicans certainly feed more than three miles from the colony. We further proposed to the Commission a one-mile closure to all commercial fishing on waters offshore Anacapa's north shore (where pelicans breed). Thirdly, we suggested that waters seaward to a depth of 20 fathoms immediately offshore the pelican nesting area be closed to all boat and human traffic. The latter recommendation was made to minimize boat and recreation-related sources of human disturbance on pelican breeding. The colony area itself is well protected through a restricted access "Research Natural Area" status established by the Park Service.

In the end, our last recommendation was the only one adopted by the Commission, but it was a necessary first step. An ecological reserve was established as a "brown pelican protection zone" by the California Department of Fish and Game. It is too early to tell if this protection zone has led to increases in pelican reproductive success. Forbidding access to the colony area, in our opinion, has played an important role in the relatively undisturbed recovery of Anacapa's brown pelicans on the breeding area itself. Other species on the island have benefitted as well. Because of the general knowledge of the pelican situation, due in large part to educational efforts and information disseminated by the agencies involved (along with the interest and cooperation of the media), there is a great deal of public willingness to recognize and accept the restricted access status of West Anacapa Island.

Near Santa Cruz Island (approximately six miles west of West Anacapa Island) lies Scorpion Rock, a small offshore islet which was the intermittent site of pelican nesting during the mid-1970's (and perhaps in years past) and also a regular loafing area for pelicans. Access to this islet is not regulated and it is easily approached and climbed. Pelicans have not nested there since 1974; human disturbances could be one reason. Areas such as Scorpion Rock deserve high priority for refuge or sanctuary status. In our opinion, there are still areas such as this in the Southern California Bight that should be acquired and (or) protected by the appropriate agencies.

The Farallon Islands, off the coast of San Francisco, are part of the U.S. Fish and Wildlife refuge system. Protection afforded by the refuge status has resulted in almost complete recoveries of most previously decimated seabirds nesting there [1]. Giving protection to island or coastal colonies and roost sites can control human access and disturbance, but future considerations of marine bird conservation must also include protection of food resources and feeding areas. This is perhaps the greatest challenge to marine wildlife managers. Certainly the time for more intense and sensitive marine bird conservation has come.

General Conclusions

The California brown pelican remains an important and central conservation issue on the California coast mostly because of what it represents. A conspicuous bird recognized and enjoyed by most coastal dwellers, the brown pelican is an indicator of a wide variety of marine wildlife conservation perspectives ranging from biological to emotional. As an "indicator" the brown pelican fits the following categories:

A *biological indicator*. Brown pelicans have been shown to be a sensitive indicator of a wide variety of real and potential problems common to marine wildlife species in general. While the local breeding population is recovering, California brown pelicans as well as other marine wildlife are still at risk from a host of human activities.

A *biopolitical indicator*. They also represent in principle the biopolitics and mechanics of the management of the much broader offshore wildlife resource.

A *regional indicator*. Pelicans are representative of a natural area that is threatened and surrounded by especially demanding and powerful special interests.

A *need indicator*. Much is known from research about brown pelicans. Yet much more information is needed on pelicans and other species to determine where they fit into southern California's offshore environment and how and where they are most vulnerable, and how they can best be protected.

It is clear from the case of the California brown pelican that we can use the power of endangered species to affect a series of coastal ecological problems which extend far beyond the scope of saving a single breeding population. Endangered species may play their most important role in attracting attention to and winning support for broad management efforts. Only through a comprehensive approach to resource utilization can we hope to save either these endangered species or our coastal environment.

Acknowledgments

We are grateful to the California Department of Fish and Game (with state aid from the U.S. Fish and Wildlife Service), and the U.S. National Park Service for direct support for brown pelican research. The University of California at Davis and Bodega Bay Institute provided indirect support. We thank Ralph Swanson (USFWS) and Dennis Raveling (UCD) for technical advice; and Sharon Newsome (Coastal Alliance) for stimulating this review. Much of our general knowledge and interpretation on the Endangered Species Act comes from the many issues of the *Endangered Species Bulletin*, published by the USFWS. We have also gleaned much "inside" information from conversations with agency people as well as from their files and news releases; these are impossible to cite. Biological statements on pelicans are based on data soon to be published. Interpretations are mostly our own, but not without outside influence.

A New Ecology
for the Coast

EUGENE P. ODUM

EUGENE P. ODUM

is Callaway Professor of Ecology, Alumni Foundation Professor
of Zoology, and Director of the Institute of Ecology at the
University of Georgia in Athens, Georgia. He was responsible for
the establishment of the Marine Institute at Sapelo Island, the
Institute of Ecology, and the Savannah River Ecology Laboratory
which the University operates for the U.S. Department of Energy.
In 1968 Dr. Odum was named Georgia's Scientist of the Year,
and was elected to the National Academy of Sciences in 1970.
He has received two international awards — La Institute de la Vie
Prize in 1975, and the Tyler Ecology Award in 1977. Dr. Odum
is the author of two widely used textbooks, *Fundamentals of
Ecology* and *Ecology*, as well as more than 150 papers for scientific and popular journals.

Dr. Odum has pioneered ecosystem ecology as a new "integrative" science. His related research interests are ecological
energetics, estuarine and wetland ecology, ornithology, and resource economics.

Efforts to design sound plans for the coast can be a first test of what Dr. Eugene Odum terms the new ecology, an ecology that looks not just at one species or one habitat, but at entire ecosystems. In this concluding essay, the "Father of Ecology" weaves together several strands that appear in earlier essays: particularly the need for systems-level study and analysis.

Only scientific teamwork that unites the skills and insights of physical and biological scientists, says Dr. Odum, can fully study and evaluate complicated ecosystems like coastal wetlands. Too often, specialization in science has hindered the understanding of such larger systems.

Dr. Odum discusses the new ecology as it applies to coastal estuaries and marshes. He further advocates a new kind of economic accounting to evaluate the worth of natural systems. Such accounting, he believes, must include not just the market value of individual components in an ecosystem — the fish, the timber, the land. It must also include the true value of what has been called the "free work of nature," work such as water purification, and the vital formation of life-supporting oxygen, nitrogen, and other gases.

Dr. Odum's sophisticated approach blends physical, biological, and economic science. He challenges us to use these new mechanisms to resolve the stubborn conflicts that now divide environmentalists and developers.

TOO OFTEN environmental problems are looked upon as cases to solve one at a time or after the fact. Yet if complex ecosystems like those of our coasts are to be managed in nondestructive ways, we can no longer consider one component — one species, one eroding beach, one polluting substance — at a time. Just as the dynamics of a forest cannot be grasped by studying, however minutely, a single species of tree, so the dynamics of a coastal wetland cannot be understood — or the potential effects of changes judged — by isolated study of any single component. The theory that the whole is more than the sum of the parts is not only an ecological paradigm, but common sense wisdom as well.

Specialization in scientific discipline has too often worked against the study of whole systems. Science and technology in the past half century have been so preoccupied with reductionism that larger supraindividual systems have suffered benign neglect. We are abysmally ignorant of the ecosystems of which we are dependent parts.

An ecosystem consists of living components (organisms, including humans) and non-living components (the physical environment) functioning together as a whole according to well-defined natural laws. To understand such complicated interrelated operations and systems, science must not only be reductionist in the sense of seeking to understand phenomena by detailed study of smaller and smaller components. Science must also be synthetic and holistic in the sense of seeking to understand large components as functional wholes.

This is the mission of what we have called the new ecology. It seeks to study and understand, through a team approach, entire ecosystems. Ecosystem-level study can reveal emergent properties of the whole that tend to be missed in piecemeal study of individual components.

Scientists work together best when motivated by some common idea, even if — or perhaps, especially if — that idea is controversial in scientific circles. It has been our experience at the Institute of Ecology at the University of Georgia that setting up ecosystem-level hypotheses promotes team research at field laboratories. Individual investigators with their differing skills and approaches are greatly stimulated by having some common hypothesis to test, and soon become enthusiastic in developing their own approaches to a basic problem.

When we set up a hypothesis on detritus in salt marshes, it resulted in creation of an almost completely new field of microbial ecology. It soon became evident that traditional microbiological techniques used in the laboratory were completely unsuited for the study of natural systems. Isolating organisms in pure cultures has practically no meaning when it comes to understanding how microorganisms actually function in ecosystems. Thus a whole new set of techniques had to be developed before the roles of various organisms could be understood.

System-level hypothesis has helped integrate physical and biological sciences in the search for a better understanding of such priceless resources as our estuaries and other wetlands. In a sense, the search for emergent properties, that is, phenomena which are discoverable only when the whole system is considered, becomes the great challenge of environmental science today.

Just as the new ecology requires teamwork by scientists in different disciplines, so does it require new efforts to understand and quantify the true values of nature's work. The new ecology demands that economic cost accounting of natural environments like the coastal zone include not just "market value" of such things as fish and real estate. It must also include public values — those things like water purification that until now have been considered the "free work of nature." Only in such a way can the life-support value of natural environments be factored into land use decisions.

Efforts to design management programs for the coastal zone offer a promising arena in which to test this new, broader scientific approach to environmental issues. Ultimately, developing a new ecology for the coast may show a way to protect, preserve, and in some cases restore, stressed systems which support life on our planet.

While the need for a broader systems approach exists for all ecosystems, it may be urgent for coastal wetlands. Decisions based on market value alone have led to the filling in and destruction of priceless wetlands, ecosystems that are a vital part of the global life-support system.

Wetlands

Wetlands have a very special value in maintaining global cycles of carbon, nitrogen, sulfur, and other vital elements. In this zone, microbial transformations "gasify" many important nutrients, such as nitrates, sulfates, and organic matter. Wetlands production of methane, carbon dioxide, ammonia, and gaseous nitrogen compounds recycle these important elements into the atmosphere. Recent studies indicate that methane plays an important role in maintaining the ozone layer that provides the protective shield vital to life on earth.

Wetlands have many other values on a local or regional scale. Included among these benefits are the role wetlands play as water storage reservoirs which assist in maintaining groundwater levels; as filters which keep agricultural or industrial chemicals out of surface waters; as scenic open spaces; and as sources of food for fish and wildlife.

Wetlands should be preserved whenever possible for the very good reason that their multiple value is usually greater on an area basis than any other kind of landscape which might replace the swamp or marsh. In other words, existing wetlands should not be converted to another use unless it can clearly be shown that the new use will contribute more to life support and the quality of human existence.

The difficulty which arises here stems from the heart of an un-fettered supply-and-demand economy: the pricing system. This approach to public policy decisions is ineffective in preserving the natural environment as long as life support and other benefits of undisturbed natural systems are not weighed in land use decisions.

Cost-accounting techniques for industrial, commercial, and residential interests are well developed, and can bring strong pressures to bear because of the nearly universal acceptance of evaluation techniques which show the cash value of a particular management alternative. Against these evaluation techniques, conservationists and natural resource economists have been at a disadvantage because of the difficulty of translating the value of natural or undeveloped areas into monetary terms. Frequently, therefore, the alternative management decision of leaving land in its natural state is not adequately defended nor seriously considered.

The irreversible character of many development decisions within a pricing system that weights short-term economic considerations alone tends to promote development of man-made systems beyond the optimum. That is, we tend to build to a point of rapidly diminishing returns. As an integral part of the new ecology, we must extend economic accounting to include what has heretofore been considered the free work of nature. Nowhere is the need more apparent than in attempting to assess the true value of coastal wetlands.

What Is Wetland Worth?

Tidal marshes are particularly vulnerable to capricious development because many of the real values of the marshes are not

TABLE 1. Hierarchical and Chronological Summary of Wetland Values.

| | | Economic Values as Percent Total | |
| | | Market System | Extended (Internalized) |
Hierarchy	Value Categories		
Population Level	1. Fish and Wildlife and other Component Values	100%	5%
Ecosystem Level	2. Hydrological Values		
	3. Productivity Values		
Global Level	4. Waste Assimilation Values	0%	95%
	5. Atmospheric Values		
	6. Life Support Value, as an Integrative Summation		

recognized, or accrue some distance from the marsh itself [20].*
Coastal marashes and other shallow water production areas (reefs,
seaweed and seagrass beds, etc.) all over the world export mineral
and organic nutrients that support much of the production of the
adjacent estuarine and coastal waters. Furthermore, estuaries serve
as a nursery ground for commercially important coastal fish and
shellfish. Even though the marsh may be privately owned, the
production of that marsh does not accrue directly to the owner,
but to a commercial fishery, perhaps many miles away. Thus the
true value of a flowing-water exporting system must be based on
a much broader cost-accounting than is usually employed in real
estate evaluation.

There are ways to scale economic and ecological values which
at first sight might seem incapable of comparison. Accordingly,
we will review the experimental, analytical, and other evidence of
values in order to develop better methods of coastal management
in the public interest. Major categories of wetlands values are
listed in Table 1, arranged in an order which roughly parallels a
geographical ranking on local, regional, national, ·and global

*The numbers in brackets correspond to references listed in the Reference Section in the
back of the book under the heading "A New Ecology for the Coast," p. 179.

levels. Also, the sequence is more or less a chronological listing since component level values were the first to be recognized. The possibility that wetlands may play a significant role in atmospheric stability and in the maintenance of global life-support systems is just now being considered.

As we are all too painfully aware, higher-level values, which largely accrue to society as a whole rather than to the individual owner, are outside or external to the market system. In the market, money enters the picture only when salable products or services (such as game, fish, timber, recreation) occur as byproducts of the functioning of the wetland ecosystem. All other values are generally written off by economists as "free goods and services," even though economists forever caution us that there is really no such thing as a free lunch.

Economists are in general agreement that the market system, which is quite efficient when it comes to allocating man-made goods, often fails to function in the public interest when it comes to allocation of natural resources. Such a "market failure" is especially evident when it comes to life-support "goods and services," which, by and large, are accorded no value or are grossly underpriced in comparison to man-made goods and services. Typically, as shown in Table 1, 100 per cent of the market value of wetlands is based on component level values — even though this category may amount to only a small percentage of the total real value of the wetlands.

As yet, there is no consensus among economists, or anyone else for that matter, on how to correct these market failures. One set of suggestions involves pollution taxes and/or charges for use of "the commons." While these "quick-fix" measures would help, they would be inadequate.

One approach we have suggested is to extend economic cost-accounting to include the work of nature as well as the work of man [5]. Private and public values can both be expressed in monetary terms if energy is used as a common denominator. By using energy as a common denominator, one can first assess the life-support or other useful work going on in a natural area in terms of energy flow [17]. Then, since money and energy are counter-flows, one can convert energy flow (corrected or weighted for quality) to equivalent monetary units. For tidal wetlands, we estimated that the total value is 20 times the dollar value of the seafood byproducts (hence the 95 to five ratio in Table 1 [19]. While there is some disagreement over the particulars of this kind of analysis, all parties agree that a serious "market failure" occurs when it comes to evaluating natural environments and to allocating natural resources in general. If we are to correct this failure, society must be convinced that all of the values listed in Table 1 are real, and that they contribute substantially to the quality of human life.

failure" occurs when it comes to evaluating natural environments and to allocating natural resources in general. If we are to correct this failure, society must be convinced that all of the values listed in Table 1 are real, and that they contribute substantially to the quality of human life.

Let us briefly review the evidence for substantial value at each of the levels, as well as for the whole wetland.

Wildlife Value.   Fish and wildlife values of wetlands were the first to be recognized and generally accepted by the public. Among the first wetlands to be preserved for their intrinsic values were those providing habitat for water birds and fish. Thousands of acres of fresh water marshes were preserved because of their value as waterfowl habitat. This occurred at a time in our history when drainage of marshes and swamps was considered progress. Among the first wetlands in Florida and Louisiana to be given permanent protective status were those set aside to save the egrets when they were an endangered species.

The discovery that coastal wetlands were nursery grounds for commercial seafood species provided further incentive for protective legislation, which has now been enacted by most coastal states. Due to natural characteristics, wildlife values dominate in fresh water wetlands, while fishery values dominate in brackish and saline wetlands. Overall, it has not been difficult to translate fish and wildlife values into terms the public understands — namely, money. One suspects, at times, that monetary values for fish and wildlife are inflated by conservationists and sportsmen eager to justify preservation — as, for example, estimates of the amount of money the "average" sportsman spends on gear and commercial services.

Fish and wildlife are not the only components or products of wetlands that may have a potential market value. In Sweden, serious consideration is being given to harvesting field-dried stalks of the marsh reed *Phragmites* and grinding them into a powder to be used as fuel to generate electricity. A 1978 study suggests that in a country that has to pay the high price for imported fossil fuel, the reed fuel could compete favorably with oil as an electricity source [1].

It is important to note that we are dealing with the values of component parts of the wetlands, not of the whole. Component values, even though they may represent only a small part of the theoretical total, often have been sufficient in the past to promote preservation in the absence of strong economic pressure to drain or fill. However, as land prices rise, and the demand for agricultural and urban-industrial sites increases, it is clear that component values alone will not be sufficient, in most cases, to justify preservation of extensive wetlands areas. We will need to consider the value of the complete ecosystem.

New Ecology Values.   First, a word about system-level properties as measured through the new ecology. G. W. Salt, in a recent commentary, suggests that these properties-of-whole (holistic attributes) are best considered in two quite different categories. The first, *collective properties*, are merely a summation of the behavior of component parts, while *emergent properties* are those new properties resulting from the integration of components [22].

Emergent characteristics are not discernible from observation of components alone. In other words, a collective property is a sum of parts, while an emergent property is more than a sum of parts. Just as the properties of water are not predictable from the properties of hydrogen and oxygen (the components), so emergent properties of biological systems are discernible only from observation of the whole unit (the ecosystem under discussion). Species diversity of a community is an example of a collective property since it is a summation of the relative abundances of species components. The symbiotic relationship of animals and algal plants in a coral reef which creates a unique mineral recycling system that enhances productivity is an example of an emergent property.

The Hydrologic Cycle

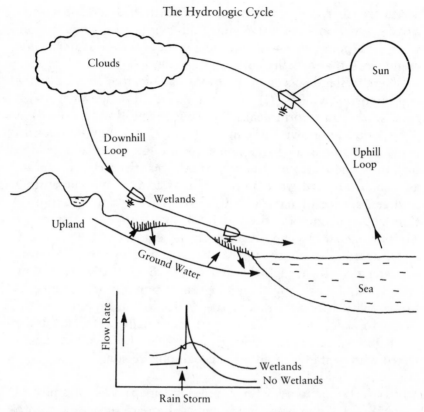

Figure 2. From an energetic standpoint, the hydrologic cycle consists of two loops, as shown in the upper diagram. Where wetlands intersect the downhill or runoff loop, they may modulate or dampen the effect of storms by reducing peak flow rate and maintaining flow during dry periods, as shown in the lower diagram. Wetlands are also interchange points between surface and ground water flows, and the potential energy in the water flow may enhance productivity (see text for further explanations).

The value of wetlands as water reservoirs, as links between surface and groundwater, and as modulators and filters in the downhill portion of the hydrologic cycle has been recognized for some time, but only recently have hydrologists begun to document in a systematic manner these potential hydrologic values. It is also evident that hydrology is the chief outside or "forcing" function that controls wetland structure and function. As shown in Figure 2, the hydrologic cycle consists of two loops: (1) an uphill one

driven by solar energy, involving evaporation, desalination, and
cloud formation; and (2) a downhill loop of rain and runoff,
where the potential energy stored by the uplift is available for
useful work that benefits both man and nature.

Where wetlands occur in the runoff circuit, they may have several important effects: (1) downhill surface flow may be moder-
ated, so that rainstorm peaks are reduced and flow continues in
dry periods, as shown in Figure 2; (2) wetlands may function as
either discharge or recharge points for ground water; and (3) the
quality of the water may be improved since the wetland can act
as a solar-powered water purification system (again constituting
a "free" service of nature that is external to economic transactions). As evidence for the latter, we may cite a 1970 study of
Tinicum marsh in Pennsylvania, which demonstrated that appre-
ciable amounts of phosphate, nitrate, and ammonia were removed
as water flowed through the marsh [6]. Some of the water flow
energy may be used by the biological community to enhance its
productivity. It is clear that we need detailed information on the
degree to which these useful services are actually performed under
the highly variable soil, geologic, and vegetative conditions associated with wetlands in different geographic regions.

Wetlands Productivity. Raymond Lindeman's classic study of
Cedar Bog Lake in Minnesota launched an era of biological productivity studies in the 1940s and 1950s [9]. It was soon discovered that many wetlands were more productive than adjacent
upland ecosystems. While there are many factors, such as nutrients, climate, soil, or sediment conditions, that influence productivity, a common denominator factor that seems to have a major
and generally positive effect is water flow. Water currents act as
an auxiliary energy subsidy that circulates nutrients, food, and
waste products within the system, thereby allowing organisms to
use more of their productive energy for growth. The wetland thus
benefits from the coupling of two forms of solar energy, direct
and hydrologic.

The general positive correlation between tidal amplitude and
productivity (as indicated by maximum standing crop) in coastal
marshes is shown in Figure 3A. The wide scatter of points indi-

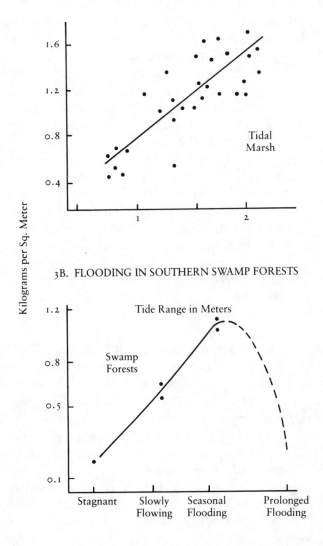

3A. TIDAL AMPLITUDE AND PRODUCTIVITY IN COASTAL MARSHES

Tidal
Marsh

Kilograms per Sq. Meter

3B. FLOODING IN SOUTHERN SWAMP FORESTS

Tide Range in Meters

Swamp
Forests

Stagnant   Slowly   Seasonal   Prolonged
          Flowing Flooding   Flooding

Figure 3. A. The generally positive relationship between tidal amplitude and annual dry matter accumulation (net production) in Atlantic coast *Spartina alterniflora* salt marshes. Data from Steever, *et al.* (1976). B. The effect of four different flooding regimes on annual dry matter production of southern swamp forests. The five data points are from Conner and Day (1976); the broken line portion of the curve is hypothetical.

cates that secondary factors, as previously mentioned, often modify the response to tidal energy. The effect of different flooding regimes on productivity of southern swamp forests is shown in Figure 3B. These and other data suggest that moderate water flows and normal seasonal flooding enhance productivity of adapted communities while stagnant water conditions, on the one extreme, and abrasive or prolonged flooding, on the other, depress it.

It is suspected that tidal fresh water uplands, which occur in the upper reaches of riverine estuaries, may be among the most productive of wetlands, because the vegetation benefits from moderate tidal energy but does not have to contend with salt stress or storm tides. In an experimental study, R. E. McDermott found that the growth of tupelo gum seedlings was greater when water levels were fluctuated than when held constant [10]. Evidence from the field that periodic flooding of floodplains is beneficial is presented by W. C. Johnson and colleagues, who found that incremental growth of maples, elms, and ash was reduced when normal spring floods were eliminated by an upstream dam [7]. Unfortunately, dikes built to protect man-made structures often result in converting natural subsidy into man-made stress.

Waste Assimilation. There is growing evidence that many types of wetlands have a special capacity to assimilate treated sewage and industrial wastes and to filter chemicals in the runoff from agricultural fields. Large wetlands in watersheds of urban and agricultural regions may have a high value to society simply as solar-powered, self-maintaining tertiary (final phase) treatment systems. On Long Island, a team from Brookhaven National Laboratory introduced treated sewage wastes into three types of natural ecosystems: a forest, an old-field, and a fresh water marsh-pond complex. The latter proved to have the best assimilative capacity [26]. In Massachusetts, researchers found that salt marshes were able to retain substantial amounts of introduced nutrients [24].

In Florida, after several years of intensive study, it was demonstrated that cypress dome wetlands provided a practical means for disposing of treated sewage effluents from adjacent residential communities. Nutrients were quickly taken up by the aquatic biota

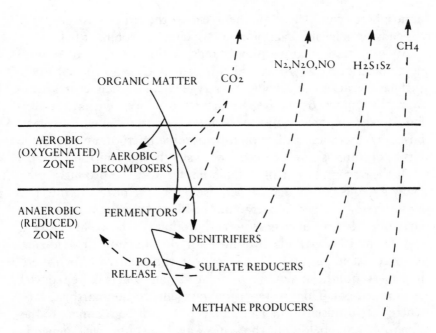

Figure 4. Major microbial decomposition and recycling in wetlands sediments. The four major anaerobic decomposers gasify, and thereby recycle to the atmosphere, carbon, nitrogen, and sulfur. Phosphate is also converted from insoluable sulfide forms to soluable forms that are again available to plants and other organisms.

and cypress trees or filtered as they moved through soil and sediment from the center of the dome to the periphery. Furthermore, the cypress dome was shown to have a greater long term economic value when used in this manner than would be the case if the wetlands were drained and converted to pine culture [18].

Wetlands and Stability. Other functions of the natural tidal marsh are more difficult to quantify, but no less real. Perhaps the most important of these is the role of the marsh in global cycles of nitrogen and sulfur. The continuing normal function of the biosphere depends on the chemical reduction of carbon, nitrogen and sulfur, which are incorporated into all living tissues. While carbon reduction occurs through photosynthesis in oxidizing atmosphere, completion of the cycle of the other two elements depends on microbial action in a reducing environment [3].

An important feature of wetlands is the presence of a well-developed anaerobic zone, which is usually close to the substrate surface. Because the aerobic, or oxygenated, zone is correspondingly thin, much of the organic matter produced within the wetland (including that imported from adjacent systems) is decomposed by anaerobic rather than by aerobic microorganisms. As a result, decomposition proceeds more slowly than on the uplands, with the accumulation of organic matter and the production of many gaseous byproducts, which rise out of the ooze and into the atmosphere. The serial interaction of four of the most important anaerobes that produce gaseous end products is shown in Figure 4.

Tidal marshes are ideally suited for the function of oxidizing nitrogen of biological origin to nitrate in the oxidized layer, where it diffuses into the anaerobic, or reduced, zone and is there reduced to nitrogen gas. Tidal waters carry nutrients to the marsh surface where they diffuse through a thin layer of oxidized sediment to the anaerobic zone below. In the same way, the sulfur cycle depends on the reduction of sulfates in the anaerobic muds to sulfur and sulfides. Thus impressive evidence points to the importance of the coastal anaerobic muds to continued normal functioning of global cycles of nitrogen and sulfur. Clearly wetlands are not just nutrient sinks, but also function as recycling systems for those elemental cycles of the gaseous type that have a reservoir pool in the atmosphere.

There are still other marsh functions worth mentioning for which cost accounting is yet to be established. A salt marsh is an important buffer against storms. In particular, it absorbs the enormous energy of storm waves and acts as a water reservoir for coastal storm waters, thus reducing damage farther inland. Some idea of the protective value of a wide band of energy-absorbing marshes and barrier islands is seen in the increasing national cost for "disaster relief" in coastal areas where these natural protective "breakwaters" are either lacking or where they have been filled in, or bulkheads have been built for housing or other development. Marsh and island-protected coasts suffer comparatively little damage even in fierce hurricanes. Rising costs of coastal development are very often the result of ill-planned modification of natural protective systems, not the result of increased storm activity.

Apples and Oranges

How to add up the values that accrue on the various levels remains an unsolved problem when it comes to the practical assessment of a specific situation. However, there are a number of approaches to this "apples and oranges" type of problem: the common denominator approach; the scaling and weighting approach; and the replacement value approach. Energy flow could be used as a common denominator. Possible water flow could serve as another common denominator, around which all values could be clustered and summed up.

The replacement value approach seems to be more acceptable to economists than the energy approach, because one can often make an accurate estimate of the monetary costs associated with the loss of a "free" service performed by a natural ecosystem such as a wetland. For example, one can calculate what it would cost a city to install tertiary waste water treatment plants to replace the tertiary treatment work performed by a large river or estuary. The cost in such a case, and hence the value of the natural system, can run into millions of dollars.

A difficulty with all these methods is that many of the useful functions performed by wetlands cannot be evaluated on a small scale. Assessing the hydrologic, wildlife, and other values for a large wetland, such as the Okefenokee Swamp, is reasonably straightforward. Such is not the case with assessing value for a one-acre tidal marsh or for a narrow strip of floodplain. In the latter cases, the habitats are best evaluated and managed as functional parts of larger ecosystems, such as a watershed. Numerous patches and strips of wetlands provide a desirable diversity within the watershed and act as buffers and filters between man's urban and agricultural development and his most vital natural resource: water.

Many coastal wetlands of limited area have their greatest value at the state or regional level, and hence should be dealt with politically and economically at such levels. A small patch of wetland considered only as an isolated local ecosystem will in most cases have such a small value by whatever method of assessment one might adopt that preservation cannot possibly compete with other land use demands. When such a patch can be shown to be a vital functional part of a larger ecosystem, a much stronger case for preservation can be made.

New Ecology Teamwork is Essential

In the real world monetary values are always going to weigh heavily in any decision regarding human use of the environment. The need to shift thinking and action to the ecosystem level, and to factor in long-term and life-support values becomes more evident as the practices of technology assessment and environmental impact analysis assume more important roles in coastal decision-making. Questions asked and answers found can be quite different depending on the level of assessment. For example, a thoroughly competent study restricted to the technical performance of a fission nuclear reactor could well show that this method of power generation is reasonably safe. Since technologists have stressed safety as *the* limiting factor and the public, for a time, logically followed in making safety *the* issue, then a favorable technology assessment of the safety problem became, for a time, a powerful signal for government and industry to launch massive development of this form of atomic energy. Yet a total assessment of such a plant that includes economic and environmental components (and covers the whole chain of events from mining to waste disposal) shows that as a first-generation attempt to utilize atomic power the light-water fission reactor is badly flawed technology, and thus not yet ready to play a major role in power production, especially where alternatives are available.

The ultimate holistic approach to preparing environmental impact statements would integrate both economic and environmental values. Regrettably, environmental and economic assessments usually are made by different teams or individuals. Not only do these teams rarely communicate with one another, each also tends to restrict evaluation to his own preconceived narrow world of the natural or human environment, respectively, ignoring the fact that it is the interaction between these systems that is of paramount importance. Environmental and economic assessors should work together, using methods that scale economic and ecological values. A closer liaison between ecology and economics makes sense because in so many cases actions which benefit the general environment also benefit the general economy in the long run.

The time has come to think in terms of a "reciprocal design" in which engineer and ecologist work together to create a harmonious coupling of the urban-industrial and life-support systems. Typically, the first response to pollution problems involves a regulatory approach: limits to waste discharges are set, to be adhered to if a firm or municipality is to receive a legal permit to operate. As a second step, complementing the regulatory process, reciprocal design emphasizes cooperation rather than confrontation between producers and consumers. Everyone, then, would have a common goal of maintaining a stable and high quality living space.

For example, Industry A creates a highly alkaline waste product containing heavy metals, toxic organics, degradable organic matter and inorganic salts. Reciprocal design would require the industry to design the whole process, including in-plant treatment facilities, to reduce pollution, as shown in Figure 5. The responsibility of the applied ecologist who is hired to work with the industry would be two-fold: (1) to inventory the assimilative capacity of the surrounding waters, forests, marshes, or other environment into which the treated effluent must eventually be discharged; and (2) to establish seminatural buffer ecosystems, such as holding ponds filled with vegetation, in which the effluents will reside until concentrations reach low enough levels to be "safely" discharged into the general environment.

We have seen that the need is not just to integrate the physical and biological sciences into the study of whole systems, it is also to integrate life support values into the economic decision-making process affecting ecosystems. Although the concept of the ecosystem and the general idea of the oneness of humans and nature have been widely accepted as a theory, society has yet to put such theory into practice. As long as the supply of resources and environment exceeded demand, society has not deemed it necessary

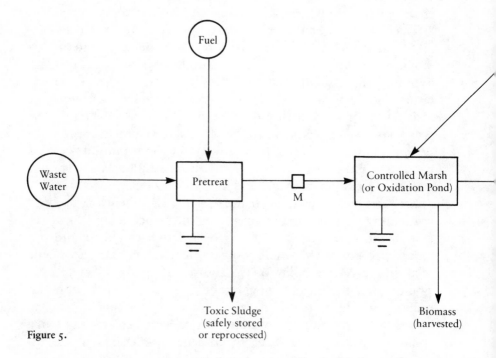

Figure 5.

Fuel

Waste Water

Pretreat

M

Controlled Marsh (or Oxidation Pond)

Toxic Sludge (safely stored or reprocessed)

Biomass (harvested)

to practice ecosystem management because problems could be solved one at a time as they appeared. True ecosystem management — that is, decision-making based on optimizing the whole — will take time to organize.

The new ecology, of course, must provide the basic theory for this necessary evolution in practice. In the meantime, there is much to be said for a procedure that combines a few carefully selected systems-level properties that monitor the performance of the whole, with selected "red-flag" components such as a game species or a toxic substance that, in themselves, have direct importance to the general public.

For now the groundwork can be laid. At the national level, the current effort to mount a program of research and management

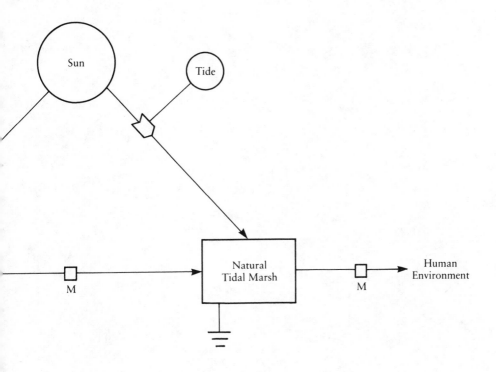

for the coastal zone may be the first major test of whether we are yet ready to combine the best of reductionist and synthesist science as a basis for rational decisions. Experience in mounting team research at the ecosystem level suggests that one or more major theories or paradigms that can be tested (and refuted, if possible) must provide a focus if the coastal zone effort — which of necessity must involve local, state, regional and federal groups — is to be a truly scientific enterprise and not just another series of expensive and frustrating inventories.

Even a partial success at coastal zone management could have a favorable global impact by demonstrating that action based on holistic values and properties is a viable alternative to development on the basis of competitive exclusion alone.

References

Rising Sea, Shifting Shores
Orrin Pilkey and Mark Evans

1. Bruun, P. 1962. Sea-level rise as a cause of shore erosion. *Journal of the Waterways and Harbors Division, American Society of Coastal Engineers* 88: 117.
2. Clark, John, J. S. Banta, and J. A. Zinn. 1980. *Coastal Environmental Management*. The Conservation Foundation. 161 pp.
3. Dolan, R. B., B. Hayden, and H. Lins. 1980. Barrier Islands. *American Scientist* 68: 16-25.
4. Emery, K. O. 1980. Relative sea levels from tide-gauge records. *Proceedings of the National Academy of Science, U.S.A.* 77(12: 6968-6972.
5. Hicks, Steacy D. 1981. Long period sea-level variations for U.S. through 1978. *Shore and Beach* 49: 26-29.
6. Hoyt, J. H. 1967. Barrier Island Formation. *Geological Society of America Bulletin* 78: 1125-1136.
7. Kaufman, W. and O. Pilkey. 1979. *The Beaches are Moving*. Garden City. N.Y.: Anchor Press/Doubleday.
8. Leatherman, S. P. 1979. *Barrier Islands*. Academic Press. 325 pp.
9. ———. 1979. *Barrier Island Handbook*. National Park Service, Washington, D.C.
10. Marshall, E. 1980. By flood if not by fire, CEQ says. *Science* 221: 463.
11. Oceanus. 1980. *The Coast* 23(4). 67 pp.
12. Pilkey, O. H., O. H. Pilkey, and R. Turner. 1975. *How to live with an island*. North Carolina Science and Technology Research Center. 150 pp.
13. Pilkey, O. H., W. J. Neal, O. H. Pilkey and S. R. Riggs. From *Currituck to Calabash: living with North Carolina's Barrier Islands*. North Carolina Science and Technology Research Center. 244 pp.

Oil and Fish: Can They Coexist?
Robert W. Howarth

1. Addy, J. M., D. Levell, and J. P. Hartley. 1978. Biological monitoring of sediments in Ekofisk oilfield. *Conference on Assessment of Ecological Impacts of Oil Spills, A.I.B.S.*, Keystone, Colorado.

2. Bumpus, D. F. 1976. Review of the physical oceanography of Georges Bank. *I.C.N.A.F. Res. Bull.* 12: 119-134.

3. Bureau of Land Management. 1977. *Final Environmental Statement for OCS Sale #42*. U.S. Dept. of Interior.

4. Butler, J. N. 1978. Marine Pollution: How big a problem? In: Vernber, F. J., E. B. Altekruse, and S. O. Butler (eds.), *Conference on Oil Tanker Transportation: An Interdisciplinary Analysis of National and International Policy and Practice*. Univ. of South Carolina.

5. Colton, J. B., and R. F. Temple. 1961. The enigma of Georges Bank spawning. *Limnol. Oceanogr.* 6: 280-291.

6. Farrington, J. W. 1980. An overview of the biogeochemistry of fossil fuel hydrocarbons in the marine environment. In: Petrakis, L., and F. Weiss (eds.), *Advances in Chemistry Series, #185, Petroleum in the Marine Environment*. Am. Chem. Soc.

7. Farrington, J. W. 1979. *Testimony before the Joint Hearing on the Campeche Oil Spill before the Committee on Commerce, Science, and Transportation and Committee on Energy and Natural Resources, U.S. Senate. Dec. 5, 1979*, Serial #96-66, U.S. Gov. Printing Office.

8. Fisher, N. S. 1976. North Sea phytoplankton. *Nature* 259: 160.

9. Greve, W., and T. R. Parsons. 1977. Photosynthesis and fish production: Hypothetical effects of climatic change and pollution. *Helgolanden Wiss. Mecresunters* 30: 666-672.

10. Hall, C. A. S., R. W. Howarth, B. Moore, and C. Vorosmarty. 1978. Environmental impacts of industrial energy systems in the coastal zone. *Annual Review of Energy* 3: 395-475.

11. Howarth, R. W. 1979. *Testimony before the Joint Hearing on the Campeche Oil Spill before the Committee on Commerce, Science, and Transportation and Committee on Energy and Natural Resources, U.S. Senate, Dec. 5, 1979*, Serial #96-66, U.S. Gov. Printing Office.

12. Larson, R. A., L. L. Hunt, and D. W. Blankenship. 1977. Formation of toxic products from a #2 fuel oil by photo-oxidation. *Env. Sci. Tech.* 11: 492-496.

13. Loftas, T. 1978. Tankers: Safety in segregation. *New Scientist* 77: 348-350.
14. Longwell, A. C. 1977. A genetic look at fish eggs and oil. *Oceanus* 20: 46-58.
15. Menzel, D. W. 1977. Summary of experimental results — controlled ecosystem pollution experiments. *Bull. Mar. Sci.* 27: 142-145.
16. Milgram, J. 1979. *Testimony before the Joint Hearing on the Campeche Oil Spill before the Committee on Commerce, Science, and Transportation and Committee on Energy and Natural Resources, U.S. Senate. Dec. 5, 1979*, Serial #96-66, U.S. Gov. Printing Office.
17. Miranov, O. G. 1968. Hydrocarbon pollution of the sea and its influences on marine organisms. *Helgo. Wiss. Meeresunters* 17: 335-339.
18. National Academy of Sciences. 1975. *Petroleum in the Marine Environment.*
19. North, W. J. 1973. Position paper on effects of acute oil spills. In: *Background Papers for a Workshop on Inputs, Fates, and Effects of Petroleum in the Marine Environment.* National Academy of Sciences.
20. Parker, C. A. 1970. The ultimate fate of crude oil at sea — uptake of oil by zooplankton. *AML Rep. B* 198(M).
21. ———. 1971. The effect of some chemical and biological factors on the degradation of crude oil at sea. In: *Water Pollution by Oil.* P. Hepple (ed.). Institute of Petroleum, London.
22. Pimental, D., L. E. Hudr, A. C. Bellotti, M. J. Forster, J. N. Oka, O. D. Sholes, and R. J. Whitman. 1973. *Science* 182: 443-449.
23. Quinn, J. G., J. N. Butler, J. W. Farrington, D. C. Gordon, J. L. Laseter, and R. F. Lee. 1979. Fossil fuel compounds. In: E. D. Goldberg (ed.), *Proceedings of a Workshop on Scientific Problems Relating to Ocean Pollution.* Estes Park, Col. U.S. Dept. of Commerce, N.O.A.A.
24. Rochereau, S. P. 1976. Energy analysis and coastal shelf resource management: nuclear power generation vs. sea-food protein production in the northeast region of the U.S. Ph.D. thesis, Cornell Univ.
25. Sanders, M. L. 1978. Florida oil spill impact on the Buzzards Bay benthic fauna: West Falmouth. *Journal of the Fisheries Research Board of Canada.* 35: 717-730.
26. Sauer, T. C. 1980. Volatile liquid hydrocarbons in waters of the Gulf of Mexico and Caribbean Sea. *Limnol. Oceanogr.* 25: 338-351.
27. Teal, J. M., K. Burns, and J. Farrington. 1978. *Analyses of aromatic hydrocarbons in intertidal sediments resulting from two spills of*

#2 fuel oil in Buzzards Bay, Mass. *Journal of the Fisheries Research Board of Canada* 35: 510-520.

28. Teal, J., B. McCain, P. Jumars, J. Stegeman, and R. Howarth. 1979. Biological effects — A generic view. In: E. D. Goldberg (ed.), *Proceedings of a Workshop on Scientific Problems Relating to Ocean Pollution.* Estes Park, Col. U.S. Dept. of Commerce, N.O.A.A.

Oil, Science, and Public Policy
Howard L. Sanders and Carol Jones

1. Addy, J. M., D. Levell, and J. P. Hartley. 1978. Biological Monitoring of Sediments in Ekofisk Oilfield. *Proc. Conference on Assessment of Ecological Impacts of Oil Spills*, pp. 515-539; 14-17 June 1978, Keystone, Colorado, American Institute of Biological Sciences.

2. Bender, M. E., D. J. Reish, and C. H. Ward. 1979. Re-examination of the Offshore Ecology Investigation. *Rice University Studies* 65(4&5): 35-116.

3. Blumer, M. and J. Sass. 1972. Oil Pollution: Persistence and Degradation of Spilled Fuel Oil. *Science* 176: 1120-1122.

4. Boesch, F. F. 1973. Classification and Community Structure of Macrobenthos in the Hampton Roads Area, Virginia. *Marine Biology* 21: 226-244.

5. Boesch, F. F., M. L. Wass, and R. W. Virnstein. 1976. The Dynamics of Estuarine Benthic Communities. *Estuarine Processes* 1: 117-196.

6. Brent, C. R., H. P. Williams, W. A. Bergin, J. L. Tyyoll, and T. E. Myers. 1974. Organic Carbon, Inorganic Carbon and Related Variables in Offshore Oil Production Areas of the Northern Gulf of Mexico and in Timbalier Bay, Louisiana. Gulf Universities Research Consortium/Offshore Ecology Investigation 1 + 18 pp.

7. Burchfield, H. P., Wheeler, R. J., and W. Subra. 1974. Nutrient Analysis of Water and Sediment Samples from the Gulf of Mexico South of Timbalier Bay, Louisiana (August 1972-January 1974). Gulf Universities Research Consortium/Offshore Ecology Investigation i +.

8. Cabioch, L., J. C. Dauvin, and F. Gentil. 1978. Preliminary Observations on Pollution of the Sea Bed and Disturbance of Sub-Littoral Communities in Northern Brittany by Oil from the AMOCO CADIZ. *Marine Pollution Bulletin* 9(11): 303-307.

9. Calabrese, A. 1969. *Mulinia lateralis*: Molluscan fruit fly? *Proceedings of the National Shellfisheries Association* 59: 65-66.

10. Conover, R. J. 1971. Some Relations between Zooplankton and

Bunker C Oil in Chedabucto Bay Following the Wreck of the Tanker ARROW. *Journal of the Fisheries Research Board of Canada* 28(9): 1327-1330.

11. Day, J. H., J. G. Field and M. P. Montgomery. 1971. The Use of Numerical Methods to Determine the Distribution of the Benthic Fauna Across the Continental Shelf of North Carolina. *Journal of Animal Ecology* 40: 98-125.

12. Dicks, B. 1975. Offshore Biological Monitoring. In: *Marine Ecology and Oil Pollution*, pp. 325-440. J. M. Baker (ed.). Applied Science Publishers, Barking, Essex.

13. El-Sayed, S. 1974. Effect of Oil Production on the Ecology of Phytoplankton off the Louisiana Coast. Gulf Universities Research Consortium/Offshore Ecology Investigation i + 49 pp.

14. Farrell, D. 1974a. Benthic Communities in the Vicinity of Producing Oil Wells on the Shallow Louisiana Continental Shelf. Gulf Universities Research Consortium/Offshore Ecology Investigation. 41 pp.

15. ———. 1974b. Benthic Communities in the Vicinity of Producing Oil Wells in Timbalier Bay, Louisiana. Gulf Universities Research Consortium/Offshore Ecology Investigation + 1-9 + 14-95 pp.

16. Fish, A. G., L. M. Massey, J. R. Inabinet, and P. L. Lewis. 1974. A Study of the Effects of Environmental Factors Upon the Distribution of Selected Sandy Beach Organisms of Timbalier Bay, Louisiana. Gulf Universities Research Consortium/Offshore Ecology Investigation. i + 102 pp.

17. Grassle, J. F. and J. P. Grassle. 1974. Opportunistic Life Histories and Genetic Systems in Marine Benthic Polychaetes. *Journal of Marine Research* 32: 253-284.

18. Gulf Universities Research Consortium. (No Date). The Offshore Ecology Investigation. Gulf Universities Research Consortium. 1611 Tremont Street, Galveston, Texas. 13 pp.

19. Hartley, J. P. (In Press). Biological Monitoring of the Seabed in the Forties Oilfield.

20. Holland, A. F., N. C. Mountford, and J. A. Mihursky. 1977. Temporal Variation in Upper Bay Mesohaline Benthic Communities. 1. The 9m Mud Habitat. *Chesapeake Science* 18: 58-66.

21. Johnsson, S. 1979. Impact of Oil in the Pelagic System. In: *The TSESIS Oil Spill. A Cooperative International Investigation, Article 3, 15 pp.* Ask;o Laboratory, University of Stockholm, Sweden; Swedish Water and Air Pollution Research Institute (IVL); Spilled Oil Research Team, NOAA, U.S.A.; Energy Resources Company, Inc., U.S.A., Elmgred & Westin (eds.).

22. Kolpack, R. L. (ed.). 1971. Biological and Oceanographic Survey of the Santa Barbara Channel Oil Spill 1969-1970. *Volume II. Physical, Chemical and Geological Studies*, v + 477 pp. Allan Hancock Foundation, University of Southern California. Sea Grant Publication No. 9.

23. Krebs, C. T. and K. A. Burns. 1977. Long-term Effects of An Oil Spill On Populations of the Salt-Marsh Crab *Uca pugnax. Science* 197: 484-487.

24. Kritzler, H. 1974. Oil Production and Polychaetous Annelids in a Louisiana Estuary. Gulf Universities Research Consortium/Offshore Ecology Investigation 1 + 61 pp.

25. Laseter, J. L. and E. J. Ledet. 1974. Hydrocarbons and Free Fatty Acids Associated with Air/Water Interface, Sediments and Beaches of the Timbalier Bay and Offshore Louisiana Area. Gulf Universities Research Consortium/Offshore Ecology Investigation. 69 pp.

26. Lie, U. 1968. A Quantitative Study of Benthic Infauna in Puget Sound, Washington. U.S.A. in 1963-1964. *Fiskeridirektoratets Skrifter, Serie Havunders7okelser* 14(5): 229-556.

27. Mackin, J. G. 1973. A review of significant papers on the effects of oil spills and oilfield brine discharges on marine biotic communities. *Texas A & M Research Foundation, Project 737*, 87 pp. and annotated bibliography of oil pollution literature.

28. Massé, H. 1971a. Contribution a l'Étude de la Macrofaune de Peuplements des Sables Fins Infralittoraux des Côtes de Provence. I. La Baie de Bandol. *Tethys* 2(4): 783-820.

29. ———. 1971b. l'Étude Quantitative de la Macrofaune de Peuplements des Sables Fins Infralittoraux. II. La Baie du Prado (Golfe de Marseille). *Tethys* 3(1): 113-158.

30. ———. 1972. Contribution a l'Étude de la Macrofaune de Peuplement des Sables Fins Infralittoraux de Côtes de Provence. III. L'Anse de Verdon. IV. L'Anse de Saint-Gervais (Golfe de Fos). *Tethys* 3(2): 283-319.

31. Mertens, E. W. 1976. The Impact of Oil on Marine Life: A Summary of Field Studies: In: *Sources, Effects and Sinks of Hydrocarbons in the Aquatic Environment, Proceedings of the Symposium, American University, Washington, D.C., 9-11 August 1976.* pp. 507-514. The American Institute of Biological Sciences.

32. Michael, A. D., C. R. VanRaalte, and L. S. Brown. 1975. Long-term Effects of an Oil Spill at West Falmouth, Massachusetts. In: *1975 Conference on Prevention and Control of Oil Pollution, Proceedings, March 25-27, 1975,* San Francisco, pp. 573-582. American Petroleum Institute, Washington, D.C.

33. Montalvo, J. G. and D. V. Brady. 1974. Toxic Metal Determinations in Offshore Water Samples, Part 2. Gulf Universities Research Consortium.

34. Morgan, J. P., R. J. Menzies, S. Z. El-Sayed, and C. H. Oppenheimer. 1974. *The Offshore Ecology Investigation, Final Project Planning Council Consensus Report.* Gulf Universities Research Consortium Report No. 138, 34 pp.

35. Oetking, P. 1974. Currents on the Nearshore Continental Shelf of South Central Louisiana. Gulf Universities Research Consortium/ Offshore Ecology Investigation 10 pp., 3 tables, 25 figures.

36. Oppenheimer, C. H., B. M. Miget, and H. Kator. 1974. Hydrocarbons in Seawater and Organisms and Microbiological Investigations. Gulf Universities Research Consortium/Offshore Ecology Investigation viii + 77 + 46 pp.

37. Platt, J. 1969. What we must do. *Science* 166: 1115-1121.

38. Rachor, E. and S. A. Gerlach. 1978. Changes of macrobenthos in a sublittoral sand area of the German Bight, 1967 to 1975. *Rapport Proces-verbal de la Reunion, Conseil International pour l'Exploration de la Mer* 172: 418-431.

39. Reish, D. J. 1957. *The Relationship of the Polychaetous Annelid Capitella capitata (Fabricius) to Waste Discharges of Biological Origin.* U.S. Public Health Service Publication No. 208: 195-200.

40. Rhoads, D. C. and A. Michael. 1974. *Summary of Benthic Biologic Sampling in Central Long Island Sound and New Haven Harbor (Prior to Dredging and Dumping) July 1972-August 1973.* Prepared for Distribution to the U.S. Corps of Engineers, United Illuminating Company, and Department of Environmental Protection of Connecticut.

41. Rhoads, D. C., P. L. McCall, and J. Y. Yingst. 1978. Disturbance and Production on the Estuarine Sea Floor. *American Scientist* 66: 577-586.

42. Rosenberg, R. 1975. Stressed Tropical Benthic Faunal Communities off Miami, Florida. *Ophelia* 14: 93-112.

43. Rosenberg, R. and P. Möller. 1979. Salinity Stratified Benthic Macrofaunal Communities and Long-Term Monitoring Along the West Coast of Sweden. *Journal of Experimental Marine Biology and Ecology* 37: 175-203.

44. Sanders, H. L. 1974. The West Falmouth Oil Spill Saga. *New Engineer* 3(5): 32-41 (7 pp.).

45. Sanders, H. L., J. F. Grassle, G. R. Hampson, L. S. Morse, S. Garner-Price, and C. C. Jones. 1980. Anatomy of An Oil Spill: Long-term Effects from the Grounding of the Barge FLORIDA off West Fal-

mouth, Massachusetts. *Journal of Marine Research* 38: 265-380.

46. Scarratt, D. J. and V. Zitko. 1972. Bunker C Oil in Sediments and Benthic Animals from Shallow Depths in Chedabucto Bay, N.S. *Journal of the Fisheries Research Board of Canada* 29(9): 1347-1350.

47. Spooner, M. F. 1978. (AMOCO CADIZ Oil Spill) Editorial Introduction. *Marine Pollution Bulletin* 9(11): 281-284.

48. Straughan, D. 1976. *Sublethal Effects of Natural Chronic Exposure to Petroleum in the Marine Environment.* American Petroleum Institute. Environmental Affairs Department, API Publication N. 428: XV + 119 pp.

49. Wade, B. A. 1972a. Benthic Diversity in Tropical Estuary. *Memoirs of the Geological Society of America* 133: 499-515.

50. ———. 1972b. A Description of a Highly Diverse Soft Bottom Community in Kingston Harbour, Jamaica. *Marine Biology* 13: 57-69.

51. ———. 1976. The Pollution Ecology of Kingston Harbour, Jamaica. Part 4. Benthic Ecology. *Research Report from the Zoology Department, University of West Indies, Mona* (5)2: vi + 104 pp.

52. ———, L. Antonio, and R. Mahon. 1972. Increasing Organic Pollution in Kingston Harbour, Jamaica. *Marine Pollution Bulletin* 3: 106-110.

53. Waller, R. S. 1979. Effects of platforms on biota (invertebrates), Timbalier Bay. Gulf Universities Research Consortium/Offshore Ecology Investigation 1 + 15 pp.

54. Ward, C. H., M. E. Bender and D. J. Reish. 1979. The Offshore Ecology Investigation. Effects of Oil Drilling and Production in a Coastal Environment. *Rice University Studies* 65(4&5): x + 589 pp.

Can Marine Mammals Survive Man?
D. G. Chapman

1. Bailey, J. H. 1979. *Sea otter: core of conflict, loathed or loved.* E. L. Moro Publications.

2. Bockstoce, J. 1980. Battle of the bowheads (eskimo hunting). *Natural History* 89: 52-61.

3. Brower, K. 1979. *Wake of the Whale.* New York: Friends of the Earth/E. P. Dutton.
4. Haley, D. (ed.). 1978. *Marine mammals of the eastern North Pacific and Arctic waters.* Seattle: Pacific Search Press.
5. Kenyon, K. W. 1980. No man is benign. *Oceans* 18: 48-52. This article is about monk seals.
6. *New York Times Magazine.* 1980. Oil in troubled Alaska waters. November 9, 1980, pp. 13-24.
7. Norris, K. S. 1977. Tuna sandwiches cost at least 78,000 porpoise lives a year but there is hope. *Smithsonian Magazine* 7: 44-53.
8. Payne, M. 1979. Status of the Whales. *Living Wilderness* 43: 16-17.
9. Twiss, J. 1978. The West Indian manatee: an endangered marine mammal. *Water Spectrum* 12(1).
10. Wray, P. *The West Indian manatee* (Trichecus manatus) *in Florida.* National Technical Information Service, PB 285–410. U.S. Department of Commerce, Springfield, Virginia.

The Politics of Pelicans
Daniel W. Anderson and Franklin Gress

1. Ainley, D. G. and T. J. Lewis. 1974. The history of Farallon Island marine bird populations, 1854-1972. *Condor* 76: 432-446.
2. Anderson, D. W. 1978. Letters to the editor. *Pacific Seabird Group Bulletin* 5: 14-15.
3. ———, et al. 1975. Brown pelicans: Improved reproduction of the southern California coast. *Science* 190: 806-808.
4. ——— and I. T. Anderson. 1976. Distribution and status of brown pelicans in the California Current. *American Birds* 30: 3-12.
5. ———, J. E. Mendoza, and J. O. Keith. 1976. Seabirds in the Gulf of California: A vulnerable international resource. *Natural Resources Journal* 16: 483-505.
6. ——— and R. W. Risebrough. 1976. Brown pelican reproduction. *Science* 193: 96-97.
7. ——— and J. O. Keith. 1980. The human influence on seabird nesting success: Conservation implications. *Biological Conservation* 18: 65-80.
8. ———, F. Gress, K. F. Mais, and P. R. Kelly. 1980. Brown pelicans as anchovy stock indicators and their relationships to commercial fishing. *California Cooperative Oceanic Fishery Investigations Reports* 21: 54-61.

9. ———, F. Gress, and K. F. Mais. 1981. Pelicans and anchovies: Interactions between a seabird and its prey at the colony level. *Oikos*. In press.

10. ———, F. Gress. Status in a peripheral population of California brown pelicans. Manuscript in preparation.

11. Applegate, R. 1975. An index to Chumash place names. *San Luis Obispo County Archaeological Society Occasional Papers* 9.

12. Austin, O. L., Jr., W. B. Robertson, Jr., and G. E. Woolfenden. 1972. Mass hatching failure in Dry Tortugas sooty terns *(Sterna fuscata)*. Proceedings of the *International Ornithological Congress* 15: 627.

13. Bellrose, F. C. 1980. *Ducks, Geese, and Swans of North America*. Stackpole Books, Harrisburg, Pa.

14. Briggs, K. T., D. B. Lewis, W. B. Tyler, and G. L. Hunt, Jr. 1981. Brown pelicans in southern California: Habitat use, populations, and environment. *Condor*. In press.

15. Burger, J. 1981. Behavior responses of herring gulls *(Larus argentatus)* to aircraft noise. *Environmental Pollution, Series A* 24: 177-184.

16. California Coastal Commission. 1980. *Consistency certification summary number cc-7-80 (Chevron USA)*. California Coastal Commission, San Francisco.

17. California Coastal Commission. Files.

18. Clement, R. C. 1972. The pesticides controversy. *Environmental Affairs* 2: 445-468.

19. DeLong, R. L., W. G. Gilmartin, and J. G. Simpson. 1973. Premature births in California sea lions associated with high organochlorine pollutant residue levels. *Science* 181: 1168-1170.

20. Department of the Air Force. 1978. *Final environmental impact statement, Space Shuttle Program, Vandenberg Air Force Base, California*. U.S. Department of Defense, Washington, D.C.

21. Dickson, D. 1978. Brown pelican threat to Space Shuttle. *Nature* 274: 304.

22. Evans, W. E., J. R. Jehl, Jr., and C. F. Cooper (eds.). 1979. *Potential impact of space shuttle sonic booms on the biota of the California Channel Islands: literature review and problem analysis*. U.S. Air Force, Space and Missile Systems Organization, Contract F 04701-78-C-0060. Washington, D.C.

23. Fullerton, E. C. and M. W. Odemar. 1980. The development of fishery management strategies for northern anchovy *(Engraulis mordax)*. *Proceedings of the International Symposium on Fisheries*

Resource Allocation. European Inland Fisheries Advisory Committee. In press.

24. Furness, R. W. 1978. Energy requirements of seabird communities: a bioenergetics model. *Journal of Animal Ecology* 47: 39-53.

25. Gilmartin, W. G. et al. 1976. Premature parturition in the California sea lion. *Journal of Wildlife Diseases* 12: 104-115.

26. Gress, F. 1970. *Reproductive status of the California brown pelican in 1970, with notes on breeding biology and natural history.* California Department of Fish and Game, Wildlife Management Branch Administrative Report 70-6. 21 pp.

27. ———— et al. 1973. Reproductive failures of double-crested cormorants in southern California and Baja California. *Wilson Bulletin* 85: 197-208.

28. ———— et al. (1980) Feeding activities and prey preferences of brown pelicans breeding in the Southern California Bight. Annual report to California Department of Fish and Game. 38 pp.

29. ———— and D. W. Anderson. (1981) A recovery plan for the California brown pelican. U.S. Fish and Wildlife Service, Office of Endangered Species, Sacramento, California.

30. Herman, S. G., M. N. Kirven, and R. W. Risebrough. 1970. The peregrine falcon decline in California. I. A preliminary review. *Audubon Field Notes* 24: 609-613.

31. Hickey, J. J. 1970. Peregrine falcons, pollutants, and propaganda. *Can. Field Naturalist.* 84: 207-208.

32. Hunt, G. L., Jr. et al. 1979. Distribution, status, reproductive ecology and foraging habits of breeding seabirds. In: *Summary of marine mammal and seabird surveys of the Southern California Bight, Volume 3, Part 3, Santa Cruz and Irvine*, Regents of the University of California. pp. 1-399.

33. ————, R. L. Pitman, and H. L. Jones. 1980. Distribution and abundance of seabirds breeding on the California Channel Islands. In: *The California Islands: Proceedings of a multidisciplinary symposium*. D. M. Power (ed.). Santa Barbara Museum of Natural History, California. pp. 443-459.

34. ———— and J. L. Butler. 1980. Reproductive ecology of western gulls and Xantus' murrelets with respect to food resources in the Southern California Bight. *California Cooperative Oceanic Fishery Investigation Reports* 21: 62-67.

35. Jehl, J. R., Jr. 1973. Studies of a declining population of brown pelicans in northwestern Baja California. *Condor* 75: 69-79.

36. Keith, J. A. 1969. The DDE affair. *Can. Field Naturalist.* 83: 89-90.

37. Leopold, A. 1966. *A Sand County Almanac, with other essays on conservation from Round River.* New York: Oxford University Press.

38. MacGregor, J. S. 1974. Changes in the amount and proportions of DDT and its metabolites, DDD and DDE, in the marine environment off southern California, 1949-1972. *Fishery Bulletin* 72: 275-293.

39. May, R. M. et al. 1979. Management of multispecies fisheries. *Science* 205: 267-277.

40. Mayr, E. 1963. *Animal species and evolution.* Cambridge, Mass.: Harvard University Press.

41. National Audubon Society. 1979. *Sonic booms over San Miguel.* Audubon Conservation Topics West.

42. National Marine Fisheries Service. 1980. Report to the Pacific Fishery Management Council on the anchovy fishery for 1979-1980. *Southwest Fisheries Center Administrative Report LJ-80-10.* U.S. Department of Commerce, National Marine Fisheries Service, Washington, D.C.

43. National Oceanic and Atmospheric Administration. 1980. *Final environmental impact statement on the proposed Channel Islands Marine Sanctuary.* U.S. Department of Commerce, National Oceanic and Atmospheric Administration, Office of Coastal Zone Management, Washington, D.C.

44. Ohlendorf, H. M., R. W. Risebrough, and K. Vermeer. 1978. Exposure of marine birds to environmental pollutants. U.S. Fish and Wildlife Service. *Wildlife Research Report* 9: 1-40. Washington, D.C.

45. ———, E. E. Klaas, and T. E. Kaiser. 1979. Environmental pollutants and eggshell thickness: anhingas and wading birds in the eastern United States. U.S. Fish and Wildlife Service. Special Science Report—Wildlife No. 216: 1-94.

46. Pacific Fisheries Management Council. 1978. Implementation of northern anchovy fishery management plan: solicitation of public comments. *Federal Register* 43: 31651-31879.

47. Palmer, R. S. (ed.). 1962. *Handbook of North American birds: loons through flamingos.* New Haven: Yale University Press.

48. Power, D. M. (ed.). 1980. *The California Islands: Proceedings of a multi-disciplinary symposium.* Santa Barbara Museum of Natural History, Santa Barbara, California.

49. Raveling, D. G. 1978. Dynamics of distribution of Canada geese in winter. In: *Transactions of the North American Wildlife Natural Resources Conference* 43: 206-225.

50. Risebrough, R. W. 1969. Chlorinated hydrocarbons in marine eco-systems. *Chemical fallout*. M. W. Miller and G. G. Berg (eds.). pp. 5-23. Springfield, Ill.: C. C. Thomas.

51. ———. 1972. Effects of environmental pollutants upon animals other than man. In: *Proceedings of the Berkeley Symposium on Mathematical Statistics and Probability* 6: 443-463.

52. ——— et al. 1968. Polychlorinated biphenyls in the global eco-system. *Nature* 220: 1098-1102.

53. ———, F. C. Sibley, and M. N. Kirven. 1971. Reproductive failure of the brown pelican on Anacapa Island in 1969. *American Birds* 25: 8-9.

54. ———, B. W. deLappe, and W. Walker, II. 1977. Transfer of higher molecular weight chlorinated hydrocarbons in the marine environment. In: *Marine Pollutant Transfer*. H. L. Windom and R. A. Duce (eds.). Lexington, Ky.: D. C. Heath. pp. 261-321.

55. ——— et al. 1979. California mussel watch: 1977-1978. In: *Organic pollutants: Mussels, Mytilus californianus and Mytilus edulis, along the California coast, Water Quality Monitoring Report 79-22, Volume III*. State Water Resources Control Board, Sacramento, California.

56. Schreiber, R. W. 1980. The brown pelican: An endangered species? *BioScience* 30: 742-747.

57. ——— and R. L. DeLong. 1969. Brown pelican status in California. *Audubon Field Notes* 23: 57-59.

58. ——— and R. W. Risebrough. 1972. Studies of the brown pelican. *Wilson Bulletin* 84: 119-135.

59. U.S. Fish and Wildlife Service. 1974. *United States list of endangered fauna, May 1974*. U.S. Department of the Interior. Fish and Wildlife Service, Washington, D.C.

60. ———. 1980. *Important fish and wildlife habitats of California*. U.S. Fish and Wildlife Service. Portland, Oregon.

A New Ecology for the Coast
Eugene P. Odum

1. Bjork, S. and W. Graneli. 1978. Energy Needs and the Environment. *Ambio* 7: 150-156.

2. Conner, W. H. and J. Day. 1976. Productivity and composition of a bald cypress-water tupelo site and a bottomland hardwood site in a Louisiana swamp. *American Journal of Botany* 63: 1334-1364.

3. Deevey, E. S. 1970. In defense of mud. *Bulletin of the Ecological Society of America* 51(1): 5-8.

4. Dolan, R., P. Godfrey, and W. E. Odum. 1973. Man's impact on the barrier islands of North Carolina. *American Scientist* 61(2): 152-162.

5. Gosselink, J. G., E. P. Odum, and R. M. Pope. 1974. *The Value of the Tidal Marsh*. Center for Wetland Resources, Louisiana State University, Baton Rouge. LSU-SC-70-03. 30 pp.

6. Grant, R. R. and R. Patrick. 1970. Tinicum marsh as a water purifier. In: *Two Studies of Tinicum Marsh*. pp. 105-123. Washington, D.C.: The Conservation Foundation.

7. Johnson, W. C., R. I. Burgess, and W. R. Kreammerer. 1976. Forest overstory vegetation and environment on the Missouri River flood plain in North Dakota. *Ecol. Monogr.* 46: 59-84.

8. Koestler, A. and J. R. Smythie (eds.). 1969. *Beyond Reductionism*. London: Hutchinson.

9. Lindeman, R. L. 1941. Season food-cycle dynamics in a senescent lake. *American Midland Naturalist* 26: 636-673.

10. McDermott, R. E. 1954. Effect of saturated soil on seedling growth of some bottomland hardwood species. *Ecology* 35: 36-41.

11. Oertel, G. 1973. Observation on net shoreline position and approximations of barrier island sediment budgets. *Technical Report 78-2*. Georgia Marine Science Center, Skidaway Island, Georgia.

12. Odum, E. P. 1963. Primary and secondary energy flow in relation to ecosystem structure. In: *Proceedings of the 16th International Congress of Zoology* 4: 336-338.

13. ———. 1968. A research challenge: evaluating the productivity of coastal and estuarine waters. In: *Proceeds of the Second Sea Grant Conference*. Graduate School of Oceanography, University of Rhode Island, Kingston, R.I.

14. ———. 1969. Strategy of ecosystem development. *Science* 164: 262-276.

15. ———. 1977. The emergence of ecology as a new integrative discipline. *Science* 195: 1289-1293.

16. ———. 1979. *Ecology: The Link Between the Natural and the Social Sciences*. 2nd ed. New York: Holt, Rinehart, and Winston.

17. ———. Rebuttal (reply to a critique by L. Shabman and S. S. Batie. Coastal Zone Management Journal 4: 231-247). *Coastal Zone Management Journal* 5: 231-237.

18. Odum, H. T., K. C. Ewel, W. J. Mitsch, and J. W. Ordway. 1975. *Recycling treated sewage through cypress wetlands in Florida*. Occasional publication 1, Center for Wetlands, University of Florida, Gainesville.

19. ———— and E. C. Odum. 1976. *The Energy Basis for Man and Nature*. New York: McGraw-Hill.

20. Odum, W. E. 1970. Insidious alteration of the estuarine environment. *Trans-American Fisheries Society* 99: 836-847.

21. ————, J. S. Fisher, and J. C. Pickral. 1980. Factors controlling the flux of particulate organic carbon from estuarine wetlands. In: *Estuarine-Offshore Inactions*. Plenum Publication Company.

22. Salt, G. W. 1979. A comment on the use of the term "emergent properties." *American Naturalist* 133: 145-148.

23. Steever, E. Z., R. S. Warren, and W. A. Niering. 1976. Tidal energy subsidy and standing crop production of *Spartina alterniflora*. *Estuarine and Coastal Marine Science* 4: 473-478.

24. Valiela, I., J. M. Teal, and W. Sass. 1973. Nutrient retention in salt marsh plots experimentally fertilized with sewage sludge. *Estuarine and Coastal Marine Science* 1: 261-269.

25. Westman, W. E. 1977. How much are nature's services worth? *Science* 197: 960-964.

26. Woodwell, G., J. Ballard, J. Clinton, and E. Pecan. 1976. *Nutrients, toxins, and water in terrestrial and aquatic ecosystems treated with sewage plant effluents*. Upton, N.Y.: Brookhaven National Laboratory, BNL 50513. 35 pp.

ABOUT THE COAST ALLIANCE

The Coast Alliance is a nonprofit, tax-exempt organization made up of representatives of national and regional environmental organizations, labor unions, sports and commercial fishermen's groups, the scientific community, and civic organizations. The purposes of the Coast Alliance are to increase public understanding of the coast and to promote public policies for coast protection.

With 75 percent of the nation's population expected to be living within 50 miles of the coast by 1990, the pressures on the coast will be increasing, not abating.

Other trends foretell more rapid changes for the coast:

- The government plans to lease public lands for oil and gas development along the entire U.S. coast during the next five years.
- Mining of the ocean for valuable minerals is expected to begin this decade.
- Over a dozen proposals for development and expansion of major coal ports along the coast are under consideration by Congress.

The development accompanying the increasing population along the shore and the exploration at sea threatens the future of our coast. There must be a keen awareness of the tremendous ecological and economic value of the coast if we are not to lose this precious resource.

The Coast Alliance will work toward increased understanding and protection. Its plans for the 1980's include efforts to eliminate government subsidies for development in sensitive coastal areas and to strengthen legal protections for the coast.

Sarah Chasis
Chair, Coast Alliance

To learn more about the Coast Alliance or about getting involved in coast protection, write to:

Coast Alliance
530 7th Street, SE
Washington, D.C. 20003

In addition, a number of the organizations that support the Coast Alliance are extremely active on coastal issues; they also can be contacted. These include:

American Littoral Society
Sandy Hook
Highlands, New Jersey 07732
(201) 291-0055

The ALS is engaged in a number of activities that foster public interest in aquatic life. Its bulletin *Underwater Naturalist* includes an array of articles about coastal environments, particularly their underwater aspects. ALS issues a number of special publications relevant to coastal concerns, and arranges field trips and conferences.

Environmental Defense Fund
444 Park Avenue South
New York, New York 10016
(212) 686-4191

EDF is a national coalition of scientists, lawyers, and citizens dedicated to protecting environmental quality through legal action and public education. EDF is involved in an array of issues including wetlands protection, hazardous waste, and port development.

Friends of the Earth
530 7th Street, SE   or 124 Spear Street
Washington, D.C. 20003   San Francisco, California 94105
(202) 543-4312   (415) 495-4770

Friends of the Earth lobbies on a number of coastal issues, including the Coastal Zone Management Act, marine mammals, endangered species protection, barrier islands and offshore oil. FOE publishes books and *Not Man Apart*.

League of Women Voters Education Fund
1730 M Street, NW
Washington, D.C. 20036
(202) 296-1770

The educational arm of the LWV publishes a number of useful brochures on federal and state laws and regulations affecting the coast, including the CZMA, OCS oil and gas, and coastal hazard areas. Has local chapters.

National Audubon Society
950 Third Avenue
New York, New York 10022
(212) 832-3200

The Audubon Society has a broad array of educational activities and programs. The Society publishes a monthly magazine, *Audubon*, which often contains coastal information; has films on a number of relevant subjects; has a number of educational kits and pamphlets; organizes a film-lecture series; and manages a number of wildlife sanctuaries in coastal areas. Has local chapters.

National Wildlife Federation
1412 16th Street, NW
Washington, D.C. 20036
(202) 797-2945

The NWF publishes magazines that often contain information about coasts — *International Wildlife, National Wildlife, Ranger Rick's Nature Magazine*, and *Your Big Backyard*. The last two magazines are for youngsters. The Federation's pamphlets cover estuaries, wetlands, clean water laws, and endangered species. It prepares teacher kits and slide programs in association with the annual Wildlife Week observance (1981 theme: "We Care About Oceans").

Natural Resources Defense Council
122 East 42nd Street
New York, New York 10017
(212) 949-0049

NRDC is a national organization with a staff of environmental lawyers and resource specialists, several of whom work specifically on coastal zone management, wetlands and barrier island protection, floodplain management, and offshore oil drilling. NRDC publishes a quarterly magazine, *Amicus*.

Oceanic Society
Magee Avenue
Stamford, Connecticut 06902
(203) 327-9786

The Oceanic Society focuses on the entire marine environment with the objective of fostering informed and sensible management of ocean and coastal resources. In addition to publishing *Oceans Magazine*, the Society produces films and other educational materials.

Sierra Club
530 Bush Street
San Francisco, California 94108
(415) 981-8634

The Club is involved in a variety of coastal issues from coastal zone management to water quality to protection of specific coastal natural areas. The Club's magazine is *Sierra*. Has local chapters.

Basic Reading List

Carson, Rachel, *The Edge of the Sea*, Houghton-Mifflin Co., Boston, 1955.

Clark, John, *Coastal Ecosystem Management*, The Conservation Foundation, Washington, D.C., 1977.

Cole, John, *Striper, A Story of Fish and Man*, Little, Brown and Company, Boston-Toronto, 1978.

Culliny, John L., *The Forests of the Sea*, Sierra Club Books, San Francisco, 1976.

Kaufman, Wallace, and Orrin Pilkey, *The Beaches are Moving*, Anchor Press/Doubleday, Garden City, New York, 1979.

Myers, Jennie, *America's Coasts in the 80's: Policies and Issues*, Coast Alliance, 1981.

National Oceanic and Atmospheric Administration, *The Federal Coastal Programs Review, A Report to the President*, U.S. Department of Commerce, 1981.

Ringold, Paul L., and John Clark, *The Coastal Almanac*, W. H. Freeman & Co., San Francisco, 1980.

Simon, Anne W., *The Thin Edge*, Harper and Row, New York, 1978.

Teal, John, and Mildred Teal, *Life and Death of a Salt Marsh*, Little, Brown and Company, New York, 1969.

U.S. Department of the Interior, *National Estuary Study*, U.S. Government Printing Office, Washington, D.C., 1970.

Warner, William W., *Beautiful Swimmers: Watermen, Crabs and the Chesapeake Bay*, Penguin Books, 1977.